ISBN 958-694-009-8

Systems and Farmer Participatory Research

Developments in Research on Natural Resource Management

Centro Internacional de Agricultura Tropical
International Center for Tropical Agriculture
Apartado Aéreo 6713
Cali, Colombia

CIAT Publication No. 311
ISBN 958-694-009-8
Press run: 700
Printed in Colombia
June 1999

Systems and farmer participatory research : developments in research on natural
    resource management / edited by Sam Fujisaka ; with the collaboration
    of Annie Jones. -- Cali, Colombia : Centro Internacional de Agricultura
    Tropical, 1999.
        165 p. : illus. -- (CIAT publication ; no. 311)
        ISBN 958-694-009-8

    1. Natural resources. 2. Germplasm. 3. Plant breeding. 4. Appropriate
technology. 5. Rotational cropping. 6. Land use. 7. Research. 8. Sloping land.
9. Savannas. 10. Pastures. 11. Sustainability. 12. Green manures. 13. Cover plants.
14. Seed production. 15. Technological changes -- Latin America. I. Fujisaka, Sam.
II. Centro Internacional de Agricultura Tropical.

Contents

Page

Chapter

Foreword

Had it not been for the significant advances in agricultural productivity over the last 5 decades, the dire predictions, made in the 1950s, of widespread hunger and famine would surely have been fulfilled. Yet, despite unprecedented growth in world population, food production has kept pace. This remarkable achievement is eloquent testimony to the high payoff from the investment in science that had underpinned such a large part of the extra production.

But new challenges are now ahead. Disturbingly, public investment in agricultural science in the developing world is declining. While certainly the rapid expansion of investment by the private sector bodes well for future advances in productivity, no assurance exists that those gains will necessarily apply to crops that provide food and livelihood for the poorest.

Although population growth rates have slowed, the absolute increase in food production needed in the next 25 years, just to sustain current consumption levels, will be greater than any increase yet achieved in the history of humanity. Moreover, this increase will have to be accomplished against a backdrop of a decreasing or, at best, a maintained level of natural resources. Indeed, in some places, the practices adopted to achieve past gains are incompatible with the sustainable use of natural resources. We therefore need to induce a "doubly green revolution", as Gordon Conway, President of the Rockefeller Foundation, graphically described in a recent publication.

Inducing such a revolution is a complex challenge. To meet it, past approaches of research on tropical farming systems must yield to new, broader, ways of thinking that will enable us to develop a view that spans from a crop's genome to the entire agroecological landscape. New disciplinary mixes will be needed, and more effort focused on bringing the advances in basic sciences to bear on problems of tropical agriculture– whether these be at the level of molecular markers, decision support systems for small farms, ecological studies of agrobiodiversity, or community action for improved watershed management.

CIAT, a world leader in applying science to tropical agriculture, is at the forefront of these changes. This volume, edited by Sam Fujisaka, an anthropologist, is CIAT's first on natural resource management per se. It reflects our concern with the sustainable use of natural resources and our commitment to farmer participatory methods as an essential ingredient in the search for farming systems that will genuinely improve human welfare.

Past successes must be tempered by the fact that, even now, more than 800 million people suffer from malnutrition. Causes are both multiple and complex, and we must be realistic in our expectations of agricultural research to address this severe problem. Even so, without the continued application of science in new and imaginative ways we can little hope to reach the goal, expressed by the 1996 World Food Summit in Rome, of reducing by half the number of hungry people by 2015. The studies reported in this volume indicate the extent to which CIAT and its partners have laid the foundations toward answering this challenge.

Grant M. Scobie
Director General
CIAT

Preface

The International Agricultural Research Centers (IARCs) were formed 30 years ago to respond to predictions of global food shortages and regional famine. The Centers conducted research to improve the genetic potential of crops such as rice, wheat, and maize. New varieties and crop management practices led to increases in yields and productivity in favorable areas, allowing global food production to stay ahead of population growth.

Researchers found, however, that producing more food was not enough. Poverty still persists. The gap between rich and poor is still increasing, especially in the less favorable areas. One-fifth of the population in the developing world remains chronically undernourished. Increased pressures on Asian uplands and Latin American hillsides are degrading land through soil erosion and nutrient depletion. Tropical deforestation, in which slash-and-burn (S&B) agriculture plays a major role, continues to lead to loss of biodiversity and emissions of carbon into the atmosphere—with the latter contributing to changes in the global climate. Even favorable areas face a new generation of problems: environmental and human health problems from the use of agrochemicals; degraded irrigation systems where maintenance funds are lacking; agrobiodiversity loss

accompany the adoption of modern varieties; and commodity prices sustain their 20-year decline.

The IARCs continue to respond. Today, they are concerned with creating impact in terms of reduced poverty and a more protected environment. Research is under way to address the constraints encountered in previously bypassed areas and to deliver benefits to the rural and urban poor. At the same time, the Centers seek to contribute to the development of technologies, institutional changes, and policies that support sustainable agriculture. Major research efforts are now dedicated to integrated pest management (IPM), green manure and cover crops, alternatives to S&B agriculture, agroforestry, soil and water conservation, natural resource management (NRM) policies, and conservation of agrobiodiversity, among others.

Research at the Centro Internacional de Agricultura Tropical (CIAT) has evolved from genetic improvement of rice, cassava, forages, and beans to improvement of land use systems, integrating germplasm and NRM. CIAT's goals are to alleviate poverty and improve food security while sustaining production systems and protecting the environment. Work is conducted in partnership with an increasing variety of stakeholders. Significant attention is given to looking across levels, for example, from crop and farm to watershed and region or agroecosystem; and the issue of "scaling up" is now a major concern. More attention is being paid to the institutional and policy changes required to obtain wider impact. The use of tools such as participatory research, decision support systems, and geographic information systems has become commonplace. Impact of research is measured at different scales, for example, in terms of productivity and household food security, sustainability, carbon sequestration, biodiversity, and institutional and policy issues.

CIAT reviewed its experiences with systems research and discussed future directions in a workshop held 1-2 December 1997 at its headquarters in Palmira, Colombia. The workshop's objectives were to:

- Foster, among CIAT scientists, the exchange of experiences with different aspects of systems research;

- Analyze CIAT's experiences with farmer participatory research within a systems context;

- Identify priority themes of common interest to CIAT projects, and mandated agroecosystems and commodities;

- Discuss proposals for the future directions of systems research at CIAT; and

- Consider strategies for obtaining impact from this work.

This volume is intended to represent more than a record of the workshop's proceedings. Researchers were encouraged to spend additional time and effort in refining and improving their contributions after the workshop. They were asked to discuss achievements in terms of problem solving through systems research, reasons for successes and failures, future potential impacts, and the strategies required for achieving such impact. Several papers were further reorganized around these themes. The patience and collaboration of the authors and the inputs of the CIAT Communications Unit, especially the final editing by Elizabeth de Páez, are gratefully acknowledged.

CHAPTER 1

Introduction: Toward a New Institutional Model of Farmer Participation in Research on Natural Resource Management and Germplasm Improvement

Sam Fujisaka*

Scientists working for CIAT in Latin America, Asia, and Africa are increasingly conducting research that combines natural research management and germplasm improvement. In so doing, scientists are working in interdisciplinary teams, are helping to develop active research partnerships through networks and consortia, and are at the forefront of the continuing development and application of methods such as farmer participatory research (FPR) and geographic information systems (GIS).

Researchers were invited to analyze, present, and discuss their work at a workshop held in late 1997 at CIAT headquarters, Cali, Colombia. The workshop and this volume, based on the workshop papers, are intended to provide an opportunity for scientists to share their evolving approaches, findings, successes, failures, impacts, and lessons learned.

Specifically, the objectives of the workshop, and of this volume, are to:

- Foster an exchange of CIAT's experience with different aspects of systems research;

- Analyze CIAT's experience with FPR within a systems context;

- Identify priority themes of common interest to CIAT projects, and mandated agroecosystems and commodities;

- Discuss proposals for the future direction of systems research at CIAT; and

- Consider strategies for ensuring this work's impact.

The workshop was entitled "CIAT's experience with systems research and future directions". It examined such aspects as:

- Evolving efforts in the integration of germplasm and natural resource management (NRM) research,

- Development of work conducted by teams and in new partnerships,

- Farmer participatory diagnosis, research, and evaluation,

- New institutional approaches to participatory research, and

- The scales of research that now range from commodity improvement within a farm to coordinated multiple efforts to address ranges of problems at reference sites in selected agroecosystems.

* CIAT, Cali, Colombia.

1

The resulting chapters were not easily ordered or grouped because of the wealth of methods, problems addressed, crops, agroecosystems, regions represented, and types of systems and participatory approaches taken. Seven papers report on work in Latin America. Two papers come from each of Asia and Africa. Five papers describe work with legumes, either as a part of improved animal-feeding systems or as green manure and cover crops. Three presentations deal with efforts to improve livestock systems. Two papers discuss research on control of soil erosion with vegetative barriers. Commodities are represented by two papers: one on cassava, and the other on beans; the remaining papers deal with a variety of crops. Two papers demonstrate the use of GIS analysis. Setting the tone for much of this volume, eight papers employ and contribute to the development of FPR approaches, and two of these address participatory institutional change. The papers range from a discussion of strategic systems research, balancing on-station and on-farm research, to an account of incorporating "farmers' independent experimentation" in agricultural research. All presentations demonstrate CIAT's commitment to work in effective collaboration with a range of partners.

Systems characterization and improved problem diagnosis are cited as major goals in three of the papers. As demonstrated, characterization now implies much more than site description, analyses of farmer survey data, and synthesis of secondary data. Some researchers use remote sensing and GIS tools to look at land use dynamics and to determine "recommendation domains" for particular technologies. Others continue to conduct strategic research to determine basic biophysical processes and dynamics inherent in studied agroecosystems. Researchers

are working in a variety of ways, from traditional surveys to participatory diagnosis, to improve the understanding of problems and the identification of needed research.

Among others, the Barreto chapter (Chapter 2), "Developing a natural resource management technology for a specific agroenvironment: *Mucuna*-maize rotation on the hillsides of northern Honduras", combines available spatial and agroclimatic databases and agronomic field data to define target environments for a green manure (*Mucuna*)-maize rotation in the Atlantic region of Honduras. Farmers had developed and adopted the rotation, and it had received research attention as a sustainable NRM technology. The fear was then that the technology would be promoted in unsuitable areas. Barreto recommends a preliminary target, provides the methods for arriving at the recommendation, and suggests further research needs.

Fujisaka et al.'s chapter (Chapter 3), "Land use systems and dynamics in Pucallpa, Peru", reflects the more traditional characterization research. Nevertheless, this research combined intensive sample survey results with an analysis of a 1993 LandSat TM image to better understand land use systems and dynamics in Pucallpa, Peru. The research, which identified and compared four local user groups—slash-and-burn (S&B) forest farmers, riverine S&B farmers, small-scale cattle ranchers, and oil-palm growers—was conducted by CIAT personnel, the International Centre for Research in Agroforestry (ICRAF), and government and university agricultural research systems. The incentives underlying different farmers' resource-use decisions were analyzed. A major output is the preliminary identification of appropriate research agendas for each group. In this case, recommendations are based on both farmers' desires to increase production or the stability of production, and on more global interests pertaining to sustainable resource use, maintaining forest biodiversity, and reducing greenhouse gas emissions.

Chapter 4—"Strategic systems research for the Latin American savannas" (Friesen et al.)—describes the development and implementation of a program of partnership research for the *Llanos* of Colombia and Venezuela and the *Cerrados* of Brazil. The efforts were described as being "...focused on developing principles and on understanding the socioeconomic driving forces and biophysical processes that allow sustainable agricultural production". That is, much of the research serves to characterize the savanna agroecosystem at the process level. Among other themes, research dealt with nutrient cycling and soil quality indicators under different systems, rice-green manure rotations, and improved pastures using multipurpose legumes. The authors describe problem identification and diagnosis, research strategy and methodologies, problems, successes and failures, and lessons learned. The paper emphasizes the need for a balance of on-station and on-farm (including participatory) research, and for a focus on principles and processes to avoid problems of site specificity.

The integration of NRM and crop or commodity research is another important theme of this volume and of CIAT's current directions. Chapters 5 to 9 describe research, in which goals included improving the productivity of livestock or cassava systems on the one hand, and protecting and sustaining the respective agroecosystems on the other.

Chapters 5 to 12 also recount various experiences in developing and applying various forms of FPR. As can be seen, "participation" ranges from farmer management and feedback on their on-farm trials, to farmers' independent experimentation, to participation of farmers, local groups, and external institutions in new, needed institutional and research arrangements. Participation is also seen as a way to increase research efficiency, promote adoption of technologies, and empower farmers, and as a part of needed institutional change.

"Developing improved pasture systems for forest margins" (Lascano et al.; Chapter 5) presents a case study of partnership research in the Colombian forest margins. Farmers in the targeted area raised Zebu-crossed cattle for milk and beef on native pastures and on degraded pastures of introduced grasses. The project sought to increase livestock productivity while conserving the natural resource base. Forage legumes (largely *Arachis pintoi*) suitable for incorporation into pasture systems had been identified, but adoption had been minimal because, the authors contend, farmers were unaware of the innovation. The project developed a participatory approach, working with 16 farms, to establish experimental paddocks. The farmers managed the experimental plots and "provided the necessary feedback to the researchers". The paper candidly examines failures as well as impacts. *Ex ante* analysis indicated that improved pastures could expect high internal rates of return. However, problems included the use of *Arachis* cultivars unsuited to poorer soils, lack of success in working with farm managers on farms with absentee owners, difficulties in seed production, experimental paddocks too small to allow farmers to make a realistic evaluation of the innovation, and lack of commitment by participating NARS.

Ospina et al. (Chapter 6) present "Adapting participatory research methods for developing integrated crop management for cassava-based systems, Northeast Brazil". This research, conducted with a wide range of Brazilian partners, used FPR methods to develop, test, and facilitate adoption of integrated cassava pest and crop management. The FPR included the formation of committees for local agricultural research, pioneered in Colombia by CIAT researchers and local nongovernment organizations (NGOs). In terms of participation, farmers were involved in problem diagnosis, choice of trials, and evaluation of results. New cassava varieties and management practices were tested, evaluated, and adopted, but what perhaps represents the major success of the project was the NARS partners' conversion from doubtful at best to genuine and enthusiastic supporters of FPR approaches.

Müller-Sämann et al. discuss "Soil conservation strategies that take into account farmer perspectives" in Chapter 7. The project worked with small-scale hillside farmers in the Department of Cauca, Colombia, to test cassava-forage legume intercropping for improved nutrient cycling and soil erosion control, and contour hedgerows for soil erosion control. Given poor technology adoption, the project sought ways to overcome adoption constraints. Methods included extracting and marketing oil from citronella grass hedgerows, manufacturing and marketing brooms from broom grass hedgerows, planting blackberry between grass barrier strips, and rotations of cassava and grass-legumes. The FPR increased farmer-researcher interactions and improved the efficiency of associated on-station research. Although it tried to combine marketing opportunities with hedgerow barriers, the project admitted that demand for citronella oil, brooms,

and blackberries was too low to support wide adoption. In the end, the project was more inclined to promote the ley rotation system as a way of increasing income (through greater cassava yields) and conserving resources (through soil erosion control and improved nutrient cycling).

Turning to Asia, Howeler, in Chapter 8, describes "Developing sustainable cassava production systems with farmers in Asia". Research with partners in Thailand, Indonesia, Vietnam, and China involves new cassava varieties, improved crop management, and soil erosion control. Farmer participatory research was used to test innovations in each country where cassava, as a major crop, was grown on erosion-prone slopes, and where farmers consider erosion as a problem they would like to solve. The paper focuses on the FPR in Vietnam as a case study. It describes diagnosis, site selection, establishment of demonstration plots, selection of farmer participants and experimental treatments, trials on farmers' fields, problems encountered, and successes and failures. The conclusions again highlight (in addition to technical innovations) the importance of commitment, enthusiasm, and sufficient resources on the part of the FPR team members, their institutions, and local extension workers.

In a somewhat similar project in terms of developing regional partnerships, Stür and Horne present "Developing forage technologies with smallholders in East Kalimantan, Indonesia" (Chapter 9). The Forages for Smallholders Project works with farmers and national partners in Indonesia, Lao PDR, Malaysia, Philippines, Thailand, Vietnam, and China. The chapter discusses a case study from Indonesia. Farmers informally tested forages and cover crops in ways not necessarily foreseen by researchers. For example, cover crops were used as improved fallows, grasses for cut-and-carry, legume cover crops were intercropped with maize and cassava to reduce weeds, and forage mixes were sown. The authors concluded that "...forages cannot be promoted in isolation from the way they are grown and used on farms". Also important are site and farmer selection, in which the answers to two questions are of help:

1. Is there a problem that farmers face and want to solve and for which there are appropriate technical alternatives?

2. Are local and national commitment and resources sufficient?

For Africa, Wortmann et al. (Chapter 10) present "Farmers' independent experimentation with green manure and/or cover crops: a component of participatory research for improving Ugandan farming systems". The project worked with five Ikulwe villages in an interactive, problem-solving relationship to generate results relevant to a larger agroecological zone. Community-based facilitators, paid for by the project, worked with farmers interested in participatory research. Farmers later formed an FPR committee to guide local research. One result of the project was the recognition and perhaps encouragement of farmers' independent experimentation (FIE). Although FIE was highly variable and idiosyncratic, the project found ways to work with farmers to document such experiments and their results. FIE on green manure and cover crops "greatly improved the cost effectiveness of the research because much information was gained at little cost. Farmer participatory research should aim to stimulate FIE".

In addition to FPR, Chapters 11 and 12 deal directly and indirectly with the need and possibility of facilitating

needed institutional change, which, in its turn, is often needed to effect technological innovation.

David and Kasozi (Chapter 11) discuss "Designing sustainable, commercial, farmer seed production systems in Africa: case studies from Uganda". Few farmers in Uganda plant certified seed. The project proposed that commercial seed production by farmers could be a way to sustainably distribute and promote modern crop varieties. Main activities were assisting in organizing three "farmer seed enterprises" (FSEs), helping to investigate marketing and promotion, and examining seed quality. The project worked where demand for bean seed was high. The farmer groups were able to organize themselves, produce and sell quality seed, and make some money in the process, but scaling up seed production and serving larger markets were not achieved for several reasons. These included unfavorable seed certification policies for such small-scale producers, lack of linkages to other parts of the seed production sector, and insufficient technical training and support.

Finally, Ashby's "Institutional innovation as an entry point for system-level technological change" (Chapter 12) took the group to the frontier of innovations in NRM research and to wider meanings of "participation". The chapter discusses work conducted in Colombia in which local institutional change was viewed as necessary for technological change. In the Ovejas River watershed, upstream users' practices led to diminished water quantity and quality (through both agrochemical pollution and sedimentation from soil erosion) for downstream users. Attempts to impose resource use controls on upstream users had failed. The project worked to develop a new model of participatory watershed management in which responsibilities were devolved to local stakeholders. Two groups were formed: a watershed users' association to represent all stakeholders, and a consortium of external organizations and NGOs active in the area. Negotiation among stakeholders led to mutual agreements on the interdependent objectives and needs of different groups. As a result, and with initial help from the consortium, users from the lower and mid-level areas of the watershed were able to work with upstream users to implement soil and water conservation measures to benefit downstream users, and on development activities to benefit upstream users. The institutional intervention resulted in a new mechanism for negotiation and local action to improve NRM. The paper also discusses the formation and functioning of committees for local agricultural research and their impact in terms of research conducted, innovations adopted, and benefits received.

Centers such as CIAT started with basic crop improvement research, with new varieties developed largely by center scientists. NARS scientists conduct much of today's breeding efforts, although with contributions from the international centers. The chapters of this book span the last decade of further change as agricultural research was faced with the issue of sustainability—initially the sustainability of production gains, but more recently the protection and sustainability of the agricultural and natural systems themselves. As research turned to more marginal environments such as hillsides and forest margins and to the needs of resource-poor farmers, the benefits and beneficial forms of farmer participation have become more and more evident.

What CIAT refers to as systems research is the integration rather than coexistence of crop and NRM research, and the appropriate focusing of research to problems identified through participatory diagnosis with farmers and through new methods of systems characterization. These changes were logical and necessary as research has had to extrapolate goals from local to global levels, for example, from increasing small-farmer cassava production at location "X" to decreasing greenhouse gas emissions in the world's forest margins. Research support for international centers has decreased, NARS have strengthened, and power and responsibility are increasingly devolved to local levels. New forms of partnership research have developed and new institutional configurations are needed across levels to better represent the needs and potentials of today's recognized wide range of stakeholders.

CHAPTER 2

Developing a Natural Resource Management Technology for a Specific Agroenvironment: *Mucuna*-Maize Rotation on the Hillsides of Northern Honduras

Héctor J. Barreto*

The Project

Objectives

1. To connect existing spatial databases to improve the definition of targeted environments for natural resource management (NRM) technology interventions, using the *Mucuna*-maize rotation in Atlantic Honduras as a case study.

2. To define and map the agroenvironment where the *Mucuna*-maize rotation practice would be potentially useful in Honduras according to secondary information linked to geographic information systems (GIS).

3. To test simple simulation models for use in the study of the performance and spatial variability of *Mucuna* biomass production and yield components grown on farmers' fields in a given geographic agroenvironment (data evaluated at various sites over several years on hillside soils).

4. To identify and quantify differences in the phenology of

Mucuna accessions evaluated during the main cropping season of June-December.

Institutional relationships

Research was performed jointly by CIAT and the Centro Internacional de Mejoramiento de Maíz y Trigo (CIMMYT). Fieldwork was conducted during 1995-1996 at two experiment sites: the Centro Universitario Regional del Litoral Atlántico (CURLA) Experiment Station at La Ceiba, and farmers' fields of the villages of San Francisco de Saco and El Recreo (municipalities of Arizona and La Masica, Department of Atlantida). CURLA provided laboratory facilities for weighing and drying biomass and soil samples. At the CIAT Hillsides Project's office in Tegucigalpa, Honduras, secondary data were compiled and analyzed, using GIS. Data were provided by CIAT projects and the following Honduran national organizations: Corporación Hondureña de Desarrollo Forestal (COHDEFOR), Centro Internacional de Información sobre Cultivos de Cobertura (CIDICCO), Instituto Hondureño del Café (IHCAFE), Secretaría de Planificación, Coordinación y Presupuesto (SECPLAN), and Proyecto Desarrollo Bosque Latifoliado (PDBL). The present study is part of CIAT's PE-3 Project (Community Management

* CIAT, Cali, Colombia, and Centro Internacional de Mejoramiento de Maíz y Trigo (CIMMYT), stationed at Tegucigalpa, Honduras.

of Watershed Resources in Hillside Agroecosystems of Latin America). The Swiss Development Cooperation (SDC) provided financial support.

The Problem

Problem diagnosis

Honduras is 87% forest, which grows mostly on low hillsides (<1500 m). Soils are typically shallow, and, when deforested, prone to erosion and degradation, especially in humid environments. The hillsides of the north Atlantic region constitute one of the few remaining areas of broadleaf forest in Honduras (Figure 1). COHDEFOR (1997) reports that 5276 km^2 of broadleaf forest (19.5% of country total) remain in the Atlantida region, followed by lands used for shifting cultivation (3603 km^2), pastures (2494 km^2), other types of forest (577 km^2), and low-lying wetlands (811 km^2). Figure 2 shows the relative proportions of these land classes for the Atlantida region.

Deforestation in this region represents the most serious threat to sustainability faced by resource-poor farmers migrating from other regions of Honduras. Humphries (1996) suggested that promoting basic grain production on humid forestlands was unsustainable as a stand-alone goal because of the fragility of the natural resource base. She proposed an alternative approach of considering traditional means of intensifying basic grain production only as a transitional phase toward more agroforestry-based systems. In this context, strategic research should be focused on technologies that increase forest protection either directly (e.g., forest replanting or permanent crops) or indirectly (by keeping farmers from cutting forest to plant basic grains).

Farmers developed an improved fallow rotation *(abonera)* that uses *Mucuna* (a legume) in season A (May-September) and maize in season B (December-April). This system of annual rotation can last for more than 10 years on a given plot of land. The system has been widely diffused and adopted by farmers in the north Atlantic region of Honduras known as Atlantida (the Departments of Atlantida and Colón). This system has been widely described and promoted in Central America as a sustainable NRM technology, sometimes at the cost of neglecting other farmer-devised technologies (Flores 1994). Many examples of the *Mucuna*-maize rotation are documented from Latin America (Buckles et al. 1994). Triomphe (1996) detailed the characteristics of this rotation system for Honduras and discussed its benefits and limitations. The rotation system as described for northern Honduras is recognized as having key agroecological needs that include:

- A bimodal rainfall distribution within a long growing season (>270 days). This would allow *Mucuna* to be grown during season A and be followed by an economic crop (e.g., maize) during season B.

- Relatively fertile soils. Appropriate levels of production of *Mucuna* biomass for use as mulch can therefore be rapidly established and achieved (Triomphe 1996).

Other variations of the system include rotating individual plots within a farm to grow two maize crops per year per farm. This has been proposed as a way of helping migrant farmers maintain stable production in a given area (Humphries 1996).

However, the region seems to lack a framework for assembling this

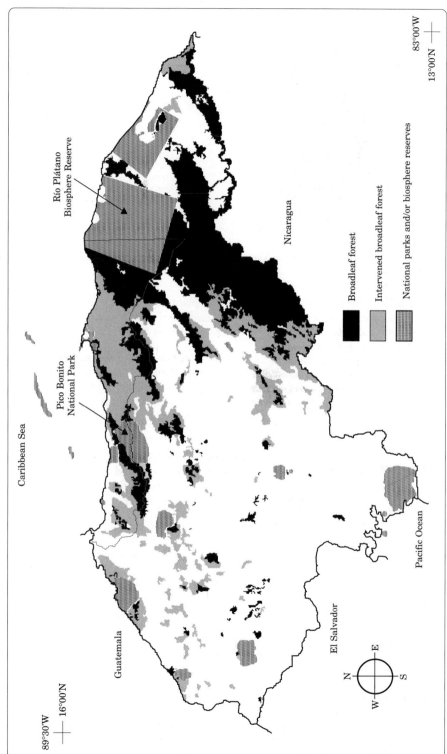

Figure 1.   The 1985 distribution of broadleaf forest, intervened areas, and national parks and/or biosphere reserves in Honduras. (Adapted from COHDEFOR 1985.)

9

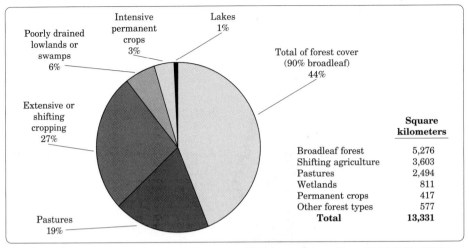

Figure 2.   Land use distribution in the Atlantida region of Honduras. (Adapted from COHDEFOR 1997.)

knowledge into useful decision support systems. These should incorporate selected elements of the environment (e.g., forest, climate, soils, and water). They should also exploit genotype x environment (GxE) interactions to both better focus technological interventions and minimize negative environmental impact in areas where most farmers have yet to adopt a given practice.

Overview of the rotation system

Researchers have described agroecological and socioeconomic features of the *abonera* system as used in Honduras (Buckles et al. 1994; Flores 1994; Sain et al. 1994; Triomphe 1996). Some of these features include:

- An extended growing season of more than 200 consecutive days where precipitation exceeds evapotranspiration (e.g., bimodal rainfall distribution >1800 mm/y).

- Soils that remain covered throughout the year. Erosion losses are reduced, and mulch from the *Mucuna* cover is sufficient to allow maize planting under zero tillage during season B (i.e., maize planted in December into mulch slashed from *Mucuna* grown in the previous season A).

- Farmers use low-input technology. Land and labor can therefore be intensified (e.g., soil conservation, improved nitrogen cycling, weed control, and lower production costs).

- Unlimited land. That is, underpopulated areas are available for shifting cultivation and rotation systems of this type.

- Ability of *Mucuna* to "re-seed" itself after each maize crop, thus decreasing production costs. The legume also changes soil biology and soil organic matter (SOM) content, creating a positive impact on soil productivity over the long term.

- Other specific features of the system already mentioned.

- Ready acceptability to farmers. Farmers had developed and spread this innovation across the humid lowlands of the Atlantic coast of Mesoamerica.

Defining a "target recommendation domain" for the rotation system

The *Mucuna*-maize rotation is an NRM technology with specific climatic requirements. Using GIS, areas can be mapped where the specified climatic requirements (temperature and rainfall) are met in an average year. CIAT has developed climate databases for Central America (Jones 1991) that facilitate identifying and mapping research problems and opportunities in NRM at the regional level (Jones et al. 1991).

An agroenvironment, or set of agroenvironments, targeted by a specific, recommended technology, is known as a "target recommendation domain". It should be considered as dynamic and as involving social factors. Resources within agroenvironments must be quantified so researchers can effectively direct agricultural technology and ensure it will cause minimum environmental degradation. Immediate action at local and regional levels is needed because of rapid changes in land use, which are especially linked to deforestation in Atlantic Honduras and Nicaragua. COHDEFOR, PDBL, and CIAT's group for Land Use Studies provide regional assessments of forest cover, using aerial photography and satellite imagery.

Issues for strategic agronomic research

Despite available knowledge, information is lacking on threshold (minimum) levels of biomass production of *Mucuna* required for successfully implementing mulch-based agriculture on the hillsides of this region.

Experimental data are needed on the production potential of this green manure and on the variability of biomass output of different genotypes of *Mucuna* (and other cover crops) under distinct cropping sequences and cycles. These data are essential for calibrating simulation models and for exploring ways to introduce green-manure/cover-crop rotations into existing systems. Although nongovernment organizations (NGOs) and local organizations have widely diffused the *abonera* system, due attention must be given to those aspects that make the system work. Research is needed on aspects that prevent this NRM practice from performing as expected.

Methods

Spatial characterization based on secondary information

Determining the target recommendation domain for a given NRM technology at farm level may not be possible with existing databases. Nonetheless, at a macro scale (1:500,000), the spatial distribution of geographic areas within Honduras that meet a combination of relevant criteria can be mapped and studied. This process would include using GIS elements based on climate databases and digital elevation models (Jones 1991), topographic and geologic features (IGN 1980), geographic distribution of broadleaf forest in Honduras (COHDEFOR 1985), and agricultural census data (SECPLAN 1994). For the Atlantida region, the criteria might include features such as:

1. Broadleaf forest cover and land-use statistics. Digitized coverages were available only for 1985 (COHDEFOR 1985; Figure 1); however, land-use statistics for the region were obtained from COHDEFOR (1997) (Figure 2).

2. Rainfall. Average amount of rain during the maize cropping season (season B) from December to March, based on long-term, interpolated-surface models (Jones 1991) (Figure 3).

3. Landscape. Areas in either well-drained plains or hillsides and mountains, based on geological characteristics (IGN 1980) (Figure 4).

4. Importance of maize. Maize production statistics at municipality and village levels during season B in the region (SECPLAN 1994) (Figure 5).

5. Selected studies. Villages where CIAT, CIMMYT, and others conducted studies to develop typologies of farmers and provide socioeconomic characterization.

These elements were assembled, using ARCVIEW©, in a way that integrated the biophysical and socioeconomic information collected from different sources.

"Chronosequence" approach to sample stratification

A chronosequence approach involves taking similar samples across space, but stratifying them according to plot history before the time of adoption of the *abonera* rotation system for given plots. This approach conveniently groups site-specific measurements (e.g., soil sampling or biomass components) across a region with relatively few characteristics to distinguish among individual sites. Triomphe (1996) devised an elaborate sampling scheme for field and plot selection for experiments conducted in "chronosequence" for this region and identified *abonera* plot histories that ranged from 1 to more than 10 years. All biomass measurements reported in

this work are linked to given plot histories.

On-farm accumulation of *Mucuna* biomass and yield components were estimated during December 1995 and again in December 1996, using the methods described by Triomphe (1996). Data were analyzed, using descriptive statistics, and analysis of variance was conducted for replicated experiments. *Mucuna* genotypes were evaluated during June-December 1995, using a collection of accessions obtained from the CIMMYT Maize Program in 1994.

Results

Identifying a "target recommendation domain" for the rotation system

The georeferenced individual elements that Figures 1 to 5 present were each defined as narrowly as possible to help improve the definition of the targeted environment for the *abonera* system. The updated (1997) map for forest cover from COHDEFOR was available only in printed form. A comparison of the existing digitized coverage (1985) with the provisional 1995 map released by COHDEFOR (1997) indicated a significant reduction in broadleaf forest in the Atlantida region. Comparisons with altitude and National Parks maps (not presented) confine most of the broadleaf forest to altitudes above 500 m and to areas declared as National Parks (Pico Bonito) or Biosphere Reserves (Río Plátano) (Figures 1 and 2).

In the digitized 1985 forest map, the class "intervened broadleaf forest" represents areas where agriculture and livestock compete with remaining stands of broadleaf forest (usually on the steepest slopes of mountains). For the purposes of this work, the *abonera* system is considered as being most useful in areas of cleared forest by

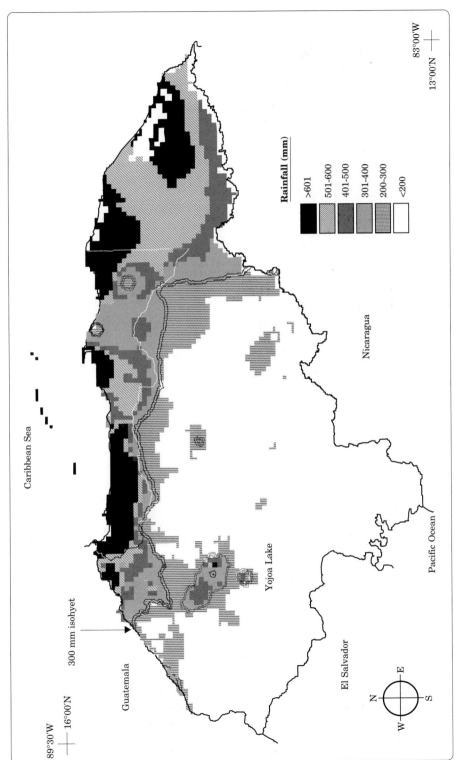

Figure 3.   Rainfall distribution during December to March (the second maize cropping season), based on reclassified interpolated surfaces according to CIAT.   (Adapted from Jones 1991.)

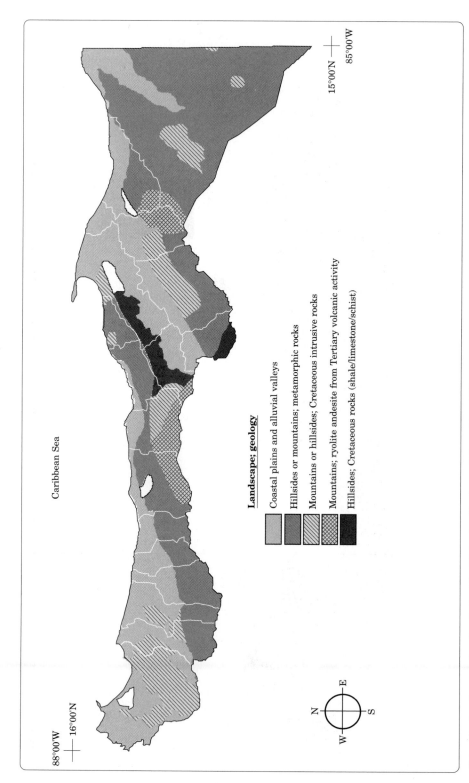

Figure 4. Landscape and geology in the Atlantida region, Honduras. (Adapted from IGN 1980.)

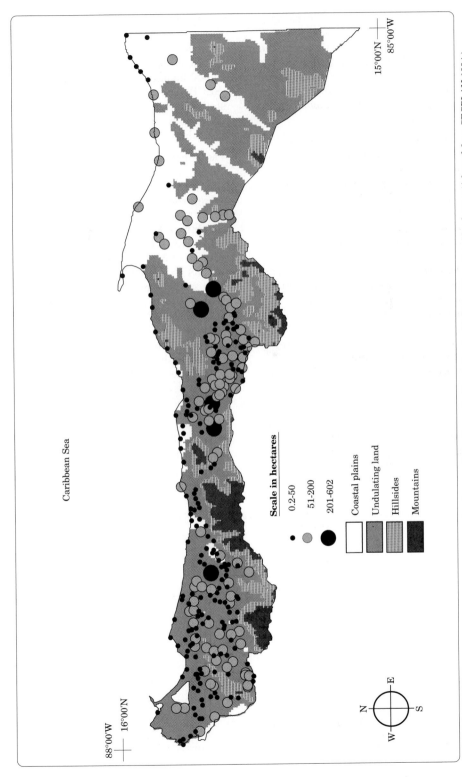

Figure 5. Area (ha) planted to monocropped maize during the second planting cycle (December-April), Atlantida region, Honduras. (Adapted from SECPLAN 1994.)

15

decreasing competition with existing forest. However, these areas also constitute the "maximum limit" for the *abonera* system, that is, if agroforestry-based systems are established in these areas, as Humphries (1996) suggests, they will push (limit) the *abonera* to cleared areas.

Figure 3 presents the average amount of rainfall during the maize cropping season (B), according to long-term, interpolated-surface models (Jones 1991). The map covers only those areas that receive more than 200 mm of rain in the period. Areas that would receive enough rainfall (i.e., more than 300 mm) in the proposed 4-month period to support an annual crop are all clearly located to northern and northeastern regions of the country, and include the Departments of Atlantida, Colón, Gracias a Dios, and part of Olancho. The exception is a small wet area toward the northwest, near Yojoa Lake.

Intensifying basic grain production through traditional means (e.g., fertilizer or pesticides) is difficult in these steep-sloped areas because of high production costs, particularly of

transport. The *abonera* system exploits a more "natural" means of crop intensification—the availability of sufficient rainfall to grow more than 17,000 ha of maize during season B (SECPLAN 1994). Table 1 gives statistics for monocropped maize production stratified by farm size in the Atlantida region.

The importance of maize production during season B cannot be underestimated when comparing the overall contribution of this system (19%) to total maize planted in Honduras. For the Atlantida region, maize grown in season B represents more than 50% of total maize planted (33,768 ha), mostly on farms smaller than 20 ha. This is because rainfall is adequate for a second cropping cycle and because farmers seek to increase grain production for both food security and cash income. Food self-sufficiency for smallholders (farms less than 5 ha) during these months is important because grain prices are usually high because of low national supplies.

Based on 1993 data, more than 54% (15,630 t) of total village production during season B was used

Table 1. Monocropped maize production for first (A) and second (B) planting cycles in the Departments of Atlantida and Colón, Honduras, 1993.[a]

Farm size (ha)	Farms (no.)		Area planted (ha)		Area harvested (ha)		Production (t)		Yield (t/ha)	
	A	B	A	B	A	B	A	B	A	B
<5	7,214	8,144	5,731	6,532	5,350	6,162	9,329	10,952	1.7	1.8
5-20	3,118	3,161	3,998	4,566	3,691	4,332	5,821	7,428	1.6	1.7
20-100	2,393	2,343	4,348	4,304	4,052	4,074	5,986	6,580	1.5	1.6
100-500	354	310	2,053	1,361	1,730	1,282	3,364	2,776	1.9	2.2
>500	17	10	467	408	408	377	1,034	1,027	2.5	2.7
Total	13,096	13,968	16,597	17,171	15,231	16,227	25,534	28,763	1.7	1.8

a. Maize intercropping systems are not included because they account for fewer than 80 ha of total maize planted.

for household consumption in the region (data not presented).

Monitoring and follow-up

Data and their corresponding software constitute a multipurpose, information tool for different stakeholders. Being able to add more recent information (e.g., updated forest maps) to such software increases the potential support available to decision makers at different levels (e.g., scientists, university and project researchers, and communities). Likewise, the software can be used as reference for planning future research in the region and, when combined with simple simulation models, can be used to study NRM problems. Chapman and Barreto (1996) addressed issues on integrating spatial databases and simulation models for studies on maize germplasm for Mexico and Central America.

Limits to mulch-based annual cropping on hillsides

In a rotation system such as the *abonera*, the amount of biomass that the cover crop accumulates affects the quantity and nutrients available to the succeeding crop. Determining the approximate amounts and variability of SOM the legume produces across

fields and years is important. Triomphe (1996) reported seasonal dry-matter accumulation for *Mucuna* of more than 11 t/ha for the Atlantida region, with little variability across sites or years. However, working in a similar system in Polochic, Guatemala, Chavez (1993) reported much smaller amounts of SOM accumulation.

Table 2 presents mean aboveground biomass components obtained from the sampling conducted in the villages of San Francisco de Saco, El Recreo, and Santa Fé. Overall, these values agree with those of Triomphe's (1996). The on-farm samplings in this study indicated lower variability of biomass production across sites (±2 t/ha), as Buckles and Barreto (1996) suggest for rotation systems. Mean values for biomass accumulation were 12.4 t/ha. From this amount of SOM, at least 7.6 t/ha are likely to be available for mulch at the onset of season B (61% of total).

Nitrogen content values for different yield components of *Mucuna* (Triomphe 1996) were used to calculate average N present in aboveground biomass as an estimate of the N resource pool at the sites at slashing time (Table 2). In the mulch alone, more than 200 kg N per ha were available at the onset of season B. The

Table 2. Biomass yield (t/ha) and apparent total N uptake in various biomass fractions found in *Mucuna* fields at slashing time in northern Honduras (average of 16 replicates).

Biomass component	Biomass mean (t/ha)	N content[a] (%)	Apparent uptake (kg/ha N)
Green leafy material + tender vines	2.1 ± 0.7	3.0	63.5
Immature and mature pods + immature seeds	1.3 ± 0.5	2.0	26.5
Old vines and stems	1.4 ± 0.7	3.0	43.4
Litter[b]	7.6 ± 1.1	2.6	200.5
Total aboveground biomass	12.4 ± 2.0		333.9

a. Average N content values reported by yield component as in Triomphe (1996).
b. Decaying organic material, including freshly shed leaves.

results presented here are to be used with caution and are suggested simply as indicators of potential *Mucuna* biomass production during season A for establishing mulch-based systems in this humid region of Honduras. The issue of defining threshold biomass accumulation values to observe residual effects on a succeeding crop remains controversial and open to debate in the scientific community because of the multiple factors that affect nutrient availability.

Exploring genetic diversity in Mucuna

Insufficient information is available on the botany and phenology of *Mucuna* cultivars grown in the Atlantic coastal area of Honduras. Duke (1981), cited by Buckles (1995), indicated that *Mucuna* is self-pollinating with rare outcrossing. Buckles (1995) also indicated that the United Fruit Company had possibly introduced the plant to the Atlantic coastal regions of Central America in the 1920s.

Based on empirical evidence, *Mucuna* characteristics appear to vary little, except in seed color (white, black, or variegated). In our 1995 study of a collection of *Mucuna* accessions obtained from CIMMYT, we detected, however, large differences in flowering, maturity dates, and biomass production among the entries (Tables 3 and 4). The results suggest ample variability in *Mucuna* flowering dates, ranging from 58 days for cultivar Georgia Velvet Bean (extra early) to the late-flowering *Mucuna* sp. from Honduras (140 days). *Mucuna* sp. 'Negra', which is widely grown throughout the Honduran Litoral Atlántico, is intermediate (110 days to flower). Maturity dates range from 126 days for *Crotalaria* to 220 days for *Dolichos* and *Mucuna* spp. Figure 6 shows seed characteristics for several accessions of *Mucuna* and other cover crops.

These findings suggest the need for additional studies to ensure sufficient genetic variability for key characteristics (such as differences in flowering dates) to be able to exploit GxE interactions. These differences in phenology also manifested in differences in aboveground biomass

Table 3. Aboveground biomass accumulation (dry matter t/ha) by different cover crops grown during the first planting cycle at the CURLA[a] Experiment Station, June 1995.

Genotype	Days after seeding[b]			
	60	120	150	180
Canavalia sp.	3.8	8.6	9.9	9.7
Crotalaria sp.	1.2	6.2	6.3	5.1
Mucuna sp. 'Georgia Velvet Bean'	2.8	9.0	10.5	na[c]
Dolichos sp.	2.6	4.8	5.1	5.0
M. pruriens utilis	4.0	4.6	5.8	4.6
Mucuna sp.	4.2	6.6	7.2	5.7
Mucuna sp. 'Negra'	3.6	6.1	6.9	5.7
Mucuna sp. 'Rayada'	4.9	7.2	8.0	7.7
Mucuna sp. 'Tlaltizapan'	3.5	6.6	7.6	5.8
Mucuna sp.	4.8	6.8	7.0	7.9

a. CURLA = Centro Universitario Regional del Litoral Atlántico, Honduras.
b. Numbers are rounded.
c. na = data not available.
SOURCE: CIAT Hillsides Project at Tegucigalpa, Honduras (unpublished data, Feb 1996).

Table 4. Days to flowering (DTF) and maturity (DTM) of different cover crops grown during the first planting cycle at the CURLA[a] Experiment Station, June 1995.

Genotype	DTF	DTM
Canavalia sp.	59	154
Crotalaria sp.	63	126
Mucuna sp. 'Georgia Velvet Bean'	58	154
Dolichos sp.	143	220
M. pruriens utilis	115	210
Mucuna sp.	140	210
Mucuna sp. 'Negra'	110	220
Mucuna sp. 'Rayada'	59	180
Mucuna sp. 'Tlaltizapan'	110	180
Mucuna sp.	120	220

a. CURLA = Centro Universitario Regional del Litoral Atlántico, Honduras.

SOURCE: CIAT Hillsides Project at Tegucigalpa, Honduras (unpublished data, Feb 1996).

accumulation by different cover crops (Table 3).

Conclusions

This work demonstrated that selected GIS of individual elements can be combined to define a preliminary "target recommendation domain" for the practice of *Mucuna*-maize rotation, or the *abonera* system. According to secondary information linked to GIS, one potential domain is Honduras. Despite the high biomass output of *Mucuna* (12.4 t/ha DM, Table 2), levels of spatial variability of biomass production and yield components were low at slashing time. This supports findings by other researchers in this region. Differences in phenology of *Mucuna* accessions were identified during the main cropping season of

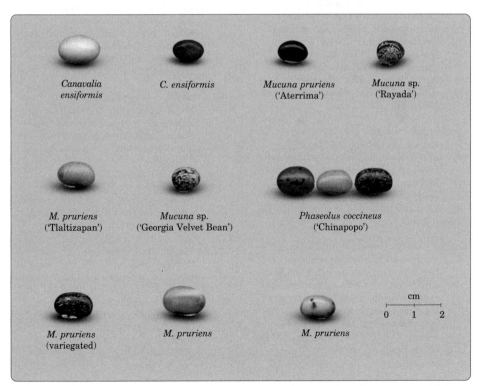

Figure 6. Seed characteristics for legume accessions evaluated at the Centro Universitario Regional del Litoral Atlántico (CURLA) Experiment Station, Honduras, 1995-1996.

June-December. This study points to the need for evaluating alternatives via GxE interaction for the species that provides the mulch.

References

Buckles D. 1995. Velvet bean: a 'new' plant with a history. Econ Bot 49:13-25.

Buckles D; Barreto H. 1996. Intensificación de sistemas de agricultura migratoria mediante leguminosas de cobertura: un marco conceptual. Doc. no. 96-06. Grupo de Recursos Naturales (GRN), Centro Internacional de Mejoramiento de Maíz y Trigo (CIMMYT), Mexico City, DF.

Buckles D; Ponce I; Sain G; Medina G. 1994. "Cowardly land becomes brave": the use and diffusion of fertilizer bean (*Mucuna deeringianum*) on the hillsides of Atlantic Honduras. In: Thurston HD; Smith M; Abawi G; Kearl S, eds. Slash/mulch: how farmers use it and what researchers know about it. Centro Agronómico Tropical de Investigación y Enseñanza (CATIE) and Cornell International Institute for Food, Agriculture, and Development (CIIFAD), Cornell University, Ithaca, NY. p 156-167.

Chapman SC; Barreto HJ. 1996. Using simulation models and spatial databases to improve the efficiency of plant breeding programs. In: Cooper M; Hammer GL, eds. Plant adaptation and crop improvement. CAB International, Wallingford, UK. p 563-587.

Chavez L. 1993. Efecto residual de la mucuna sobre el rendimiento de maiz bajo diferente sistemas de manejo. In: Buckles D, ed. Gorras y sombreros: caminos hacia la colaboración entre técnicos y campesinos. Centro Internacional de Mejoramiento de Maíz y Trigo (CIMMYT), Mexico City, DF. p 89-95.

COHDEFOR (Corporación Hondureña de Desarrollo Forestal). 1985. Mapa forestal de Honduras/mapa de áreas protegidas 1:750,000. Instituto Hondureño de Turismo and COHDEFOR, Tegucigalpa, Honduras.

COHDEFOR (Corporación Hondureña de Desarrollo Forestal). 1997. Mapa forestal 1:500,000 de Honduras. Tegucigalpa, Honduras. (Preliminary version, subject to revision.)

Flores M. 1994. The use of leguminous cover crops in traditional farming systems in Central America. In: Thurston HD; Smith M; Abawi G; Kearl S, eds. Slash/mulch: how farmers use it and what researchers know about it. Centro Agronómico Tropical de Investigación y Enseñanza (CATIE) and Cornell International Institute for Food, Agriculture, and Development (CIIFAD), Cornell University, Ithaca, NY. p 149-155.

Humphries S. 1996. Migrant, dairy farmers and agricultural land use in the humid, tropical hillsides of Northern Honduras. Internal report. CIAT, Tegucigalpa, Honduras. 78 p. (Typescript.)

IGN (Instituto Geográfico Nacional). 1980. Mapa geológico de la República de Honduras. Legend by MJ Kozuch. Peace Corps, Tegucigalpa, Honduras. 6 p. (Typescript.)

Jones PG. 1991. The CIAT climate database, version 3.7: machine-readable dataset of long-term climatic normals for the tropics. CIAT, Cali, Colombia.

Jones PG; Robison DM; Carter SE. 1991. A GIS approach to identifying research problems and opportunities in natural resource management. In: CIAT in the 1990s and beyond, a strategic plan: supplement. CIAT, Cali, Colombia. p. 73-110.

Sain G; Ponce I; Borbon E. 1994. Profitability of the *abonera* system practiced by farmers on the Atlantic coast of Honduras. In: Thurston HD; Smith M; Abawi G; Kearl S, eds. Slash/mulch: how farmers use it and what researchers know about it. Centro Agronómico Tropical de Investigación y Enseñanza (CATIE) and Cornell International Institute for Food, Agriculture, and Development (CIIFAD), Cornell University, Ithaca, NY. p 273-282.

SECPLAN (Secretaría de Planificación, Coordinación y Presupuesto). 1994. IV Censo nacional agropecuario 1993, vol II: Granos básicos. Tegucigalpa, Honduras. 217 p.

Triomphe B. 1996. Seasonal nitrogen dynamics and long term changes in soil properties under the mucuna/ maize cropping system on the hillsides of northern Honduras. Ph.D. dissertation. Cornell University, Ithaca, NY. 217 p.

CHAPTER 3

Land Use Systems and Dynamics in Pucallpa, Peru

Sam Fujisaka*, O. Madrid*, L. Hurtado*, H. Usma*,
A. Ricse**, Y. Flores**, F. Idrogo**, J. Barbarán**,
L. Arévalo***, and R. Labarta***

Introduction

Farmer-settlers in the western Amazon practice slash-and-burn (S&B) agriculture to produce annual crops such as rice, maize, cassava, and beans. In so doing, settlers convert primary tropical forest lands to other uses, including pasture for cattle production, perennial crops, and fallows for future annual cropping. Slash-and-burn agriculture of this type has contributed to deforestation, emissions of atmospheric carbon, and losses of biodiversity (Brady 1996; Fujisaka et al. 1998).

We examined land use in Pucallpa, Peru, as part of a global initiative coordinated by the International Centre for Research in Agroforestry (ICRAF) to develop "Alternatives to Slash-and-Burn".

Humid tropical forest cover characterizes Pucallpa. The site is located in the Department of Ucayali (which borders Brazil to the east) and along an east-west gradient that leads to the foothills of the Andes and along which rainfall ranges from 1800 to 3000 mm (mean 2300 mm, with rainfall increasing to the west). Wet months are February-May and September-November; dry months are June-August and December-January. Mean annual temperature is 25 °C. Soils include more favorable alluvial, riverine systems, where pH is about 7.7 and available P is 15 ppm; and higher, well-drained, forested areas of acidic (pH 4.4), low-P (2 ppm) soils. Flatter areas near the city of Pucallpa (but out of our area of interest) are poorly drained (*aguajales*) and dominated by *Mauritia* spp. palms. Although the Huanuco-Tingo María-Pucallpa highway was constructed in the 1940s, settlement became substantial in the 1970s with improvements to the highway (Loker 1993; Riesco and Arroyo 1997).

Methods

Researchers representing Peru's Instituto Nacional de Investigación Agraria y Agroindustrial (INIAA), CIAT, and ICRAF selected the Pucallpa study area. They chose the site as representative of the different types of agricultural land uses based on S&B in the broader region. A multidisciplinary team of researchers from the three institutes interviewed 151 settlers in Pucallpa in mid-1996. Interviews dealt with patterns of land

---

*   CIAT, Cali, Colombia.
**   Instituto Nacional de Investigación Agraria y
     Agroindustrial (INIAA), Lima, Peru.
*** International Centre for Research in
     Agroforestry (ICRAF), Nairobi, Kenya.

use and resource management. Responses were coded and data tabulated and presented in simple descriptive frequencies. Farmers described land use allocations for 1995/96 and for 1996/97.

Preliminary fieldwork showed that the settlers were naturally grouped by location (e.g., forest, river, and road) and by major enterprise (e.g., S&B, cattle, S&B + oil palm). Groups included farmers practicing S&B in higher forest areas; farmers living and practicing S&B along the rivers; small-scale cattle ranchers located mostly along the road connecting Pucallpa to Lima; and another subset of the forest S&B farmers who recently established oil palm as a cash crop.

A LandSat TM image from 1993, showing part of the study site, was obtained, classified, and analyzed.

Results

Migration and settlement

Of the 151 respondents, 26% (40 farmers) were from Pucallpa. Of the remaining 111 respondents, 30% (33) arrived during 1990-1995. The other 70% (78) arrived before 1989, including before the 1970s, but with fewest arriving during 1975-1984. Although, overall, the 74% (i.e., 111) of respondents who migrated to the area had been in Pucallpa for an average of 16 years, those raising cattle had arrived there, on the average, 24 years beforehand (Table 1).

Land use

Forest and riverine S&B farmers accounted for 77% of respondents (i.e., 86 farmers). The average farm size was 29 ha; in 1996, forest farms had only 27% of their land under forest, with 39% under fallow or secondary growth, 16% under pasture, 10% under perennial crops, and 8% under annual crops. Riverine farms had (in rounded numbers) more land (46%) under forest, with 26% under fallow, 12% under pasture, 7% under perennial crops, and 6% under annual crops. The 15% of all respondents, both local and migrant (i.e., 23 farmers), who had cattle had significantly larger farms (average size of 67 ha), of which only 20% was under forest. The rest was under pasture (54%), fallow (21%), perennial crops (3%), and annual crops (2%). Finally, oil-palm farmers had farms of similar sizes (average of 32 ha) as had other forest farmers, but

Table 1. Period of arrival of migrants (in percentages[a]) by main economic activity, Pucallpa, Peru.

Period of arrival	Slash-and-burn agriculture			Cattle	Oil palm	Total
	Forest (n = 32)	Riverine (n = 54)	Subtotal (n = 86)	(n = 13)	(n = 12)	(n = 111)
1990-1995	34 (11)	31 (17)	33 (28)	15 (2)	25 (3)	30 (33)
1985-1989	19 (6)	13 (7)	15 (13)	8 (1)	33 (4)	16 (18)
1980-1984	9 (3)	7 (4)	8 (7)	8 (1)	0 (0)	7 (8)
1975-1979	9 (3)	13 (7)	12 (10)	8 (1)	8 (1)	11 (12)
1970-1974	16 (5)	17 (9)	16 (14)	23 (3)	17 (2)	17 (19)
<1970	13 (4)	19 (10)	16 (14)	38 (5)	17 (2)	19 (21)
Average no. of years stayed	14	17	16	24	15	16

a. Values in parentheses refer to number (n) of respondents.

had more land under perennial crops (17%), less under fallow (24%), and least under pasture (4%).

In terms of land-use changes between 1995 and 1996 on the farms held by respondents (5249 ha), forest areas decreased from 35% to 33% and cleared areas increased from 65% to 67%. The breakdown for cleared areas is pastures increased from 24% to 25% of the total area, fallow decreased from 29% to 28%, annual crops increased from 5% to 6%, and perennial crops increased from 7% to 8%. All respondents had some cleared lands, but only 67% still had some forest. All the respondents used the cleared areas for pasture (44% of respondents), fallow (82%), annual crops (80%), and some perennial crops (84%) (Table 2).

Analysis of the LandSat TM image largely confirmed farmers' accounts: the image covered 109,100 ha, 17,300 of which corresponded to settlers' parcels and 7,400 to large-scale farms. Analysis indicated that 70% of settlers' parcels were deforested by 1993. This compared closely with the reported 67% in 1996, once a correction was made, based on parcel sizes, regarding distance of farmers' fields from the road.

Most S&B farmers cleared new forest parcels yearly (85% of forest, 57% of riverine, and 75% of oil-palm farmers) or once every 2 years (10% of forest, 29% of riverine, and 25% of oil-palm farmers). Two-thirds of the cattle ranchers, however, cleared forests once every 3 years and one-third cleared lands alternate years (Table 3). The S&B farmers (including those with oil palm) cleared, on the average, 1.5-2.0 ha per year; and the cattle ranchers cleared 2.6 ha per year (Table 4). When we compare respondents who have cattle with those who do not, the former cleared forests less often, but opened larger areas to

grow crops such as rice and cassava for sale.

Farmers reported their criteria for selecting and clearing particular forest parcels as fertile soil (43% of respondents), no flooding (29%), close to road and/or house (19%), and flatter topography (9%) (Table 5).

Farmers reported that, when they clear forest parcels, they need, per hectare, 20 days for slashing (before and after felling) and 27 days for felling, that is, a total of 47 days. For clearing fallowed parcels, they need, per hectare, 16 days for slashing and 6 days for felling, that is, a total of 22 days. Overall labor for slashing fields from forest and fallow were thus roughly equal, while labor invested in felling decreased substantially from forest to fallow.

Nearly all farmers grew rice in fields newly cleared from forest and, in the second year, if the field was not fallowed, the farmers grew cassava, maize, pasture, or other crops. In fields cleared from fallow, farmers sowed rice, maize, cassava, or banana (Table 6).

Although the amount sown fluctuated by year (Table 7), farmers, on the whole, maintained similar areas in rice, maize, and cassava.

Farmers reported actual crop yields for 1995/96 to be 1.4 t/ha of rice, 1.7 t/ha of maize, and 0.2 t/ha of beans. These were lower than their reported "normal" yields but higher than previous lowest yields of each respective crop.

Fields cleared from forest were cropped for about 2 years: 30% of the 151 respondents cultivated for 1 year, 44% cultivated for 2 years, 16% for 3 years, and 10% for more than 3 years. Fallowed lands were cultivated for about 1.3 years. Three-quarters of the

Table 2. Land use (percentage of area) by main agricultural system, Pucallpa, Peru, 1994/95 and 1995/96.

Land use	Slash-and-burn agriculture						Cattle		Oil palm		Total		Change[a]	Resp.[b]
	Forest		Riverine		Total								(%)	(%)
	94/95	95/96	94/95	95/96	94/95	95/96	94/95	95/96	94/95	95/96	94/95	95/96		
Forest	30	27	48	46	40	38	20	20	52	51	35	33	−5	67
Cleared areas	70	73	52	54	60	62	80	80	48	49	65	67	+2	100
Pasture	16	16	12	12	13	14	54	54	2	4	24	25	+0.5	44
Fallow	43	39	25	26	33	31	22	21	25	24	29	28	−5	82
Annual crops	3	8	8	6	6	7	1	2	7	4	5	6	+15	80
Perennial crops	8	10	7	7	8	10	3	3	14	17	7	8	+14	84
Total area (ha)	1443		1846		3289		1538		422		5249			
Sample size (ha)	44		71		115		23		13		151			
Average farm size (ha)	33		26		29		67		32		35			

a. Increase or decrease, in individual cases, from 1994/95 to 1995/96.
b. Resp. = percentage of 151 respondents using their farms for a given land use.

Table 3. Percentage of 52 respondents reporting a given frequency of forest clearing, by main agricultural system, Pucallpa, Peru, 1996.

Frequency (no. of years)	Slash-and-burn agriculture			Cattle	Oil palm	All
	Forest	Riverine	Combined			
1	85	57	71	0	75	69
2	10	29	19	33	25	19
3	0	9	5	67	0	8
>3	5	5	5	0	0	4
Mean	1.2	1.7	1.5	2.7	1.2	1.5

Table 4. Percentage of 93 respondents clearing a given forest area, by main agricultural system, Pucallpa, Peru, 1996.

Area (ha)	Slash-and-burn agriculture			Cattle	Oil palm	All
	Forest	Riverine	Combined			
<1.0	9	5	7	12	17	8
1.0-1.9	41	39	40	12	42	38
2.0-2.9	29	28	29	26	33	29
>3.0	21	28	24	50	8	25
Mean	1.8	2.0	1.9	2.6	1.5	1.9

Table 5. Percentage of 83 respondents reporting criteria for choosing forest field to clear and plant, by main agricultural system, Pucallpa, Peru.

Criterion	Slash-and-burn agriculture			Cattle	Oil palm	All
	Forest	Riverine	Combined			
Fertile soil	43	35	39	57	58	43
No flooding	40	30	34	0	17	29
Close to road or house	7	30	19	43	8	19
Flatter areas	10	5	8	0	17	9

Table 6. Percentage of respondents reporting main crop sown in fields cleared from forest (For; n = 100) and from fallow (Fal; n = 132), by main agricultural system, Pucallpa, Peru.

Main crop	Slash-and-burn agriculture						Cattle		Oil palm		All	
	Forest		Riverine		Combined							
	For	Fal	For	Fal	For	Fal	For	Fal	For	Fal	For	Fal
Rice	88	52	73	49	80	50	50	33	84	50	78	49
Maize	6	30	16	28	11	29	0	47	8	25	10	30
Cassava	3	10	0	2	1	5	25	0	0	17	3	5
Banana	3	3	11	9	8	7	25	7	8	0	9	6
Other	0	5	0	12	0	9	0	13	0	8	0	10

Table 7.   Changes in land use (%) from 1995 to 1996 for fields sown in 1995 by farmers in the Pucallpa area, Peru. To maintain similar areas of planting to each crop as in 1995, new fields are opened up.

1995 field planted to:	In 1996, same field[a] planted to:							
	Fallow	Cassava	Maize	Banana	Pasture	Rice	Pineapple	Other[b]
Rice (64 ha)	31 (20)	18 (12)	7 (4)	7	4	0	nd[c]	33
Maize (84 ha)	49 (41)	5 (4)	21 (18)	9	3	1	nd[c]	12
Cassava (57 ha)	46 (26)	29 (16)	0 (0)	5	4	0	8	8
Total (ha)	(87)	(32)	(22)			(<1)		

a.   Values in parentheses refer to number of hectares.
b.   Other = not including rice.
c.   nd = no data.

respondents discontinued cropping plots cleared from forest because of declining production, and almost half cited weeds as another major reason.

By combining these interview-based results with more informal field observations and discussions with settlers, we could describe each subgroup of respondents as follows:

Farmer groups

Slash-and-burn forest farmers. In 1996, forest farmers formed the group with the highest proportion of their farms that were cleared (73%). Of these, 39% were under fallow or secondary regrowth. Rice was the major crop, even though it suffered from yield-reducing diseases. These farmers had 10% of their lands under perennial crops such as citrus, *achiote* (*Bixa orellana* L.), cacao, and various fruits. A substantial number grew coca, although demand declined once domination of the area by the terrorist group, *Sendero Luminoso* ("Shining Path"), ended. To some extent, charcoal appears to have replaced coca as an income-generating alternative.

Slash-and-burn riverine farmers. Within this group, 54% of farms were cleared, of which 26% were under fallow. Rice was first planted, followed by banana (for cash) on the relatively richer soils (compared with higher forest areas). The fungal disease, sigatoka, was a major constraint, which, according to farmers, was exacerbated by defoliants and herbicides sprayed from helicopters as the Peruvian army attempted to eradicate coca fields. Flooding was both a problem and a solution (i.e., deposits of richer silts). Farmers also earned income from fish and timber from the softwood *Guazuma crinita,* which grew in fallowed land.

Small-scale cattle ranchers. These farmers had the largest parcels (average size = 67 ha), the least forest (20%), the smallest proportions of land under annual and perennial crops and under fallow (although they had the largest annual crop fields in absolute terms), and the highest proportion of land under pasture (54%). For the 15% of Pucallpa respondents having cattle, herd size was, on average, 23 head. Cattle farmers reported planting 40% of pasture area in *Brachiaria* spp. and 28% in *Brachiaria* spp. + *Pueraria phaseoloides.* Areas of native pasture, comprising *Axonopus compressus, Paspalum conjugatum*, and *Homolepis aturensis*, however, were clearly underreported. About one-third of the ranchers (39%) reported using fire to regenerate pasture at a mean interval of every 2 years; and 68% reported rotating animals to different pastures at a mean interval of 1 month. Pressure on pastures was low: 73% of these respondents maintained less than 1 head of cattle per ha, 24% had 1-2 head, and only 3% had more than 2 head per ha of pasture. Terrorism by the *Sendero* was widely reported as having led to substantial declines in cattle numbers and reduced maintenance of fences and pastures.

Slash-and-burn oil-palm farmers. Because these S&B farmers have access to plots in higher forest areas, and have taken advantage of local development projects promoting oil palm (*Eleais guineensis*), they have the largest proportion of their farms under perennial crops (17%) and the smallest under pasture (4%). The success of oil palm will depend on the development of a processing infrastructure and a demand sufficient to maintain prices at profitable levels.

Conclusions: Toward an Appropriate Research Agenda

Overall, Pucallpa farmers relied on rice as a major crop for both sale and consumption. Research to help solve upland rice disease problems, problems of soil nutrient depletion, and increased weed invasion would benefit many farmers in the area. Pucallpa farmers had a high proportion of their lands under fallow or secondary regrowth. Working with farmers on improved fallows, using trees and legumes, would appear a reasonable project.

Forest farmers of higher areas who had earned incomes from coca production (from sales and/or from wages for weeding and harvesting) are seeking new alternatives. Charcoal production—which involves the selection of suitable forest species such as *Dipterix odorata*—is one, but is probably not sustainable. Efforts to develop and promote new crops such as *camu camu* (*Myciaria dubia*) and agroindustries such as palm oil may be successful, but research is needed to carefully determine, *ex ante,* the demand for new alternatives. Farmers have already tried supposedly income-generating crops such as citrus and *achiote*, but these, unfortunately, were market failures.

Riverine S&B farmers were most concerned about diseases affecting their banana plantations and upland rice. Research to address these problems is needed.

Research in Pucallpa has long targeted cattle farmers for the introduction and testing of forage and feeding systems alternatives, including legumes such as *Arachis pintoi, Centrosema* spp., *Desmodium ovalifolium, Cratylia argentea, Stylosanthes guianensis*, and forage grasses. These settlers, however, may have little interest in using more productive forage systems as long as current pasture resources are more than sufficient, given the area's reduced herd size. However, research may be appropriate for increasing system productivity and sustainability in those few farms where a higher stocking rate is maintained than is usual in the area. Cases of such research are those of the Instituto Veterinario de Investigaciones Tropicales y de Altura (IVITA) and TROPILECHE[1].

1. For an explanation of this and other acronyms, see "Acronyms and Abbreviations Used in the Text", pages 161-165.

References

Brady NC. 1996. Alternatives to slash-and-burn: a global imperative. Agric Ecosyst & Environ 58:3-11.

Fujisaka S; Escobar G; Veneklaas E. 1998. Plant community diversity relative to human land uses in an Amazon forest colony. Biodivers Conserv 7:41-57.

Loker WM. 1993. Medio ambiente y agricultura en la Amazonia Peruana: Un experimento metodológico. In: Loker WM; Vosti S, eds. Desarrollo rural en la Amazonia Peruana. CIAT and the International Food Policy Research Institute (IFPRI), Cali, Colombia. p 13-75.

Riesco A; Arroyo M. 1997. Perfil socio-económico de la región de Ucayali. Unpublished report. Corporación para el Desarrollo Sostenible de Ucayali (CODESU) and the CIAT Rural Agroenterprises Project, Lima, Peru. 19 p.

CHAPTER 4

Strategic Systems Research for the Latin American Savannas

D. Friesen*, M. A. Ayarza**, R. J. Thomas**
E. Amézquita**, and J. I. Sanz**

Introduction

Early in the 1990s, CIAT embarked on a new strategic plan, which departed from the traditional commodity-driven approach previously dominant in the work of international agricultural research centers. The new approach placed agroecosystems at the focus of commodity and natural resource management (NRM) research (CIAT 1991a). This change was a response to the increasing concern of issues, raised in Agenda 21 (TAC 1992; UNCED 1992), on accelerating environmental degradation associated with increasing population pressures and unsustainable agricultural practices on marginal lands.

The new paradigm implied a shift from a supply- to a systems-driven approach in which germplasm improvement would be based on their requisite characteristics for systems and their constraints, rather than in isolation. However, the new strategic plan recognized that systems research is inherently site specific and risks seemingly endless analyses and location-specific research activities. To avoid this pitfall, NRM research was focused on developing principles and on understanding the socioeconomic driving forces and biophysical processes that allow sustainable agricultural production. This strategy would help extrapolate knowledge to much wider domains on well-characterized environments by using simulation models and geographic information systems (GIS). We describe the development and implementation of a strategic research program undertaken for the savanna agroecosystem, often referred to as the *Llanos* in Colombia and Venezuela, and the *Cerrados* in Brazil.

Objectives and Institutional Relationships

CIAT's 1990 strategic plan and its supplement (CIAT 1991a) identified major constraints to increased productivity and the major causes of resource degradation in the savannas. These are:

1. Low soil fertility, high soil acidity;

2. Pasture degradation, overgrazing;

3. Soil compaction and/or erosion under continuous soybean cropping;

4. Build-up of pests and weeds under intensive use;

---

*   CIAT, Cali, Colombia, and the International Fertilizer Development Center (IFDC), Muscle Shoals, Alabama, USA.
** CIAT, Cali, Colombia.

5. Water contamination through excessive use of agrochemicals;

6. Decreasing profit margins;

7. Low population density and poor infrastructure;

8. Few large-scale farmers, and these are normally absentee (especially in Colombia); and

9. Uncoordinated or nonexistent regional strategies for sustainable development (especially in Colombia).

By characterizing the biophysical and socioeconomic problems of savanna agroecosystems, specific research objectives were formulated to overcome constraints (CIAT 1991a, 1994; Sanint et al. 1992). They were to:

1. Understand the socioeconomic, organizational, and cultural aspects that condition the development and sustainability of farming systems in the savannas, and to provide a conceptual framework that allows these aspects to be integrated into local research and development institutions;

2. Analyze the future development potential and environmental consequences of predominant savanna systems (smallholders, ranches, and large-scale agriculture) under different technological, ecological, and marketing infrastructure; and policy conditions;

3. Quantify the soil and plant processes associated with changes in primary biomass productivity in typical systems and "best bet" options to develop indicators of soil quality and degradation;

4. Quantify and understand nutrient dynamics in systems to improve cycling and minimize losses; and

5. Quantify factors that influence and determine the rates of processes to calibrate, modify, or develop simulation models for overcoming site specificity and testing alternative scenarios.

The Brazil project responded dynamically to the involvement of new partners (Table 1). Studies were conducted by students from Bayreuth University (Germany) on dynamics of soil organic matter (SOM), N availability and management, and soil structure. These were executed both through the cross-sectional approach in Uberlândia and in a systems

Table 1. Institutional relationships: projects and partners of systems research projects carried out by CIAT in Colombia and Brazil.

Project	Site	Partners[a]
Agropastoral Systems Network	-	Bolivia, Brazil, Colombia, Venezuela
"Culticore" crop rotations and ley-farming systems project	Carimagua, Colombia	CIRAD, CORPOICA, IFDC, ORSTOM, Universidad Complutense de Madrid
Tillage methods project	Matazul, Colombia	COLCIENCIAS, CORPOICA
Indicators project	Meta, Colombia	CORPOICA, PRONATA
Long-term crop-pasture rotations experiment	Planaltina, Brazil	Bayreuth University, EMBRAPA-CPAC

a.   For an explanation of the acronyms, see "Acronyms and Abbreviations Used in the Text", pages 161-165.

experiment, carried out on station at Planaltina. Activities also evolved to include other on-farm sites besides Uberlândia (Maranhão, Tocantins, and Mato Grosso). In the *Llanos* of Colombia, initial collaboration also expanded. Students from the Universidad Complutense de Madrid (Spain) studied the dynamics of soil macrofauna under different land-use systems. The Agropastoral Systems Network, whose members are national agricultural research programs, provided an annual forum for exchanging ideas and progress in the development of agropastoral systems.

Problem Identification and Diagnosis

Identifying objectives and more specific problems was based on the experience, observations, and measurements that CIAT and its partners had accumulated over 25 years of research. Supplementary diagnosis was obtained through rapid rural appraisals (RRAs), field visits, and consultations with farmers, cooperatives, and research and development consortia. To characterize the savanna ecosystem and help select sites representative of the major resource management problems, GIS techniques were applied (Jones et al. 1991).

The Latin American savannas cover about 243 million hectares, mostly in Brazil (180 million hectares), followed by Venezuela (28 million hectares), and Colombia (17 million hectares), with smaller areas in Guyana and Bolivia. The largest disturbed area (about 72 million hectares) is also found in Brazil, followed by Venezuela (about 2 million hectares), mostly on well-drained land. Findings of a series of RRAs, conducted in 1990/91 in Brazil, Colombia, and Venezuela, indicated that the savannas have high potential for ecologically sound resource use and management (Sanint et al. 1992). The report distinguished between disturbed and often degraded savannas (mainly in Brazil and Venezuela) and undisturbed natural savannas (mainly in Colombia).

Figure 1 shows the "development path" in the savannas (CIAT 1995b).

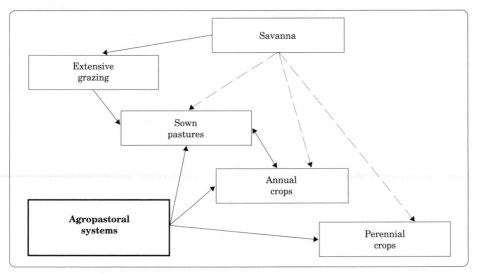

Figure 1.   Agricultural development path for savanna ecosystems in tropical South America.

Extensive grazing of natural pastures with Zebu and Zebu crossbred cattle for beef production historically dominated land use. The development path is most advanced in Brazil where frontier expansion began in the 1960s with government support in the form of subsidies, infrastructure, and policies. This dramatically changed the perception of the savannas as "lacking fertility" to their constituting one of the major agricultural frontiers that still remain in the tropics (Bourlag and Dowswell 1994).

In Brazil and Venezuela, the cropping of mostly rice, maize, soybeans, and sorghum on about 12 million hectares of savannas contributes significantly to grain production of both countries (Vera et al. 1992). However, changes in policies and subsidies, together with the debt crisis of the 1980s, have disadvantaged crop production in these areas, resulting in a need to develop more efficient, intensive production systems with a wider range of options (Sanint et al. 1992). Perennial crops such as sugarcane, coffee, oranges, and rubber trees are being introduced into the Brazilian *Cerrados*. In these disturbed savannas, watershed management and soil conservation are strategic issues for sustainable systems, because land degradation caused by soil compaction and erosion, and nutrient depletion is already evident (CIAT 1995b).

In contrast to Brazil, the Colombian savannas have "traveled" only a short distance along the development path shown in Figure 1. Most areas remain under extensive grazing on native savanna; relatively small areas are under improved pastures; and only a few enterprises have a cropping component. Figure 2 shows the historical development of the Colombian savannas.

In the unopened savannas, mainly in Colombia, the major research issue was that of expanding and intensifying agriculture into new areas while avoiding degradation. However, recent surveys revealed that such problems are occurring in the *Llanos*, although not to the extent observed in Brazil and Venezuela (Smith et al. 1997).

The relatively undisturbed native savannas represent a benchmark against which a continuum of disturbed savannas, ranging from overgrazed savannas to highly intervened, intensive production systems in various states of degradation, can be compared. This information would provide the basis for establishing guidelines to avoid environmental degradation and define land quality or early warning indicators of degradation.

Historically, CIAT research on the savannas has focused on germplasm (forages and crops) adapted to the highly infertile, acid soils that dominate this ecosystem. Understanding the impact of production on the soil resource was little emphasized. Likewise, the mechanisms of resource degradation or enhancement under different systems involving crops and forages received little attention. A better understanding of these processes is essential to extrapolate results from site-specific NRM research to other areas. Research activities therefore began to define the soil-water-plant-animal relationships in systems, and with system components, to provide guidelines and early warning signals for ecosystem stability and development. Another important objective was to relate this strategic information to farmer behavioral patterns (Sanint et al. 1992).

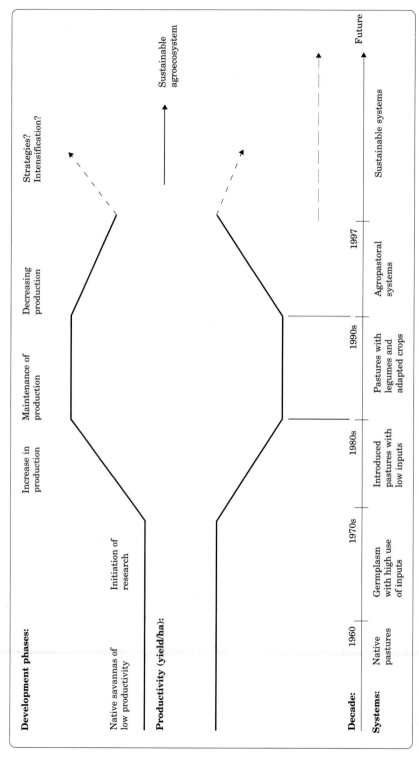

Figure 2. Summary of the historical changes occurring in the savannas of Orinoquia, Colombia (adapted after E. Amézquita, 1998, unpublished data).

Research Strategy and Methodologies

Selection of study areas

The RRAs helped select study areas representative of major land management systems and resource management problems in Brazil. A multidisciplinary team of CIAT scientists and researchers from several units of the Empresa Brasileira de Pesquisa Agropecuária (EMBRAPA) conducted the RRAs in four regions of the *Cerrados*. Secondary information was used to characterize socioeconomic factors (Jones et al. 1991). These studies identified Uberlândia as a region where the principal land-use classes occurred and, thus, as a focus of research in the savannas. The site is representative of the disturbed savannas and is complementary to the Colombian well-drained savannas (undisturbed) that CIAT has used for forage studies.

Socioeconomic determinants of agricultural intensification and resource degradation in the savannas

In 1995, the driving forces behind land-use intensification in the Colombian *Llanos* were identified through socioeconomic surveys in the area covering Puerto López and Puerto Gaitán, Department of Meta (Smith et al. 1997). Preceding surveys in 1979, 1989, and 1992 complemented collected data. Smith et al. (nda) conducted similar work in three watersheds near Uberlândia, Brazil, studying changes in land use and adoption of NRM technologies in grain production systems. Smith et al. (ndb) visited frontier regions in the *Cerrados,* interviewed key informants, and analyzed the impact of policy and technology on the dynamics of the agricultural frontier in the Amazon and savannas. They used models of land use and whole-farm livestock production to simulate development scenarios and determine the most important variables for land-use change.

Soil-plant trade-offs between production and resource conservation in conventional and improved land-use systems

Strategic research on soil-plant processes focuses on the production system. This approach is based on the hypothesis that, when placed in appropriate configurations in systems, the negative effects of individual components can counterbalance and ameliorate one another. The approach does not preclude the need to develop and evaluate individual components. But, in the systems' context, knowledge of individual characteristics is applied to seek a positive synergism in ways that protect and enhance the resource base and the use of inputs. Figure 3 illustrates the approach used to evaluate forage legumes for pure grass pastures on the *Cerrados*.

Assessing the impact of alternative configurations on the resource base has been approached through both longitudinal studies and cross-sectional analyses. The former approach has involved the use of both prototype "systems experiments" and the more traditional "factor experiments" conducted on station.

Cross-sectional analysis attempts to capture in space the effects of degradative or regenerative processes under a particular type of land use that have occurred over time and under similar edaphic and climatic conditions. Identifying a sufficiently broad range on this synthetic time scale is often difficult to achieve while maintaining adequate homogeneity in spatial variables. The confounding

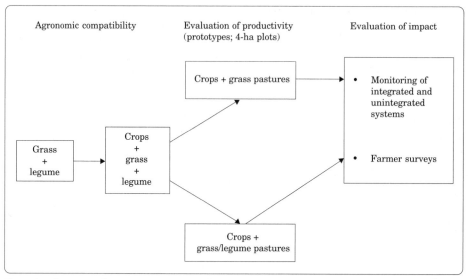

Figure 3. Strategy and sequence of activities in the development of improved agropastoral systems for the Brazilian *Cerrados* (adapted from CIAT 1997).

influences of spatial variability pose a challenge to interpreting cross-sectional data. Furthermore, although this approach offers the possibility of identifying dynamic soil properties with potential use as soil quality indicators (SQIs), definition of threshold values is much less certain. These thresholds must be more rigorously and precisely defined through controlled experiments on well-characterized sites.

Cross-sectional analysis is also limited to comparing existing systems and cannot report on the effects that untried system configurations or new soil-management technologies may have on the resource base. These latter evaluations require a more reductionist, longitudinal approach. Yet evaluating the almost limitless combinations and permutations of components and management technologies would challenge even an unlimited budget of resources and time.

CIAT's response to the challenge of system evaluation is based on

understanding and quantifying the effects of system components on soil processes, executed in the context of "best-bet" prototypes under well-controlled conditions. Such experiments are often and necessarily long term because degradative processes themselves are often slow and subtle. Nonetheless, they must be quantified before developing, modifying, and calibrating simulation models that can evaluate how changes in systems and their management affect the natural resource base. Thus, the approach for defining both indicators and predictive tools requires both opportunistic observations across the full range of existing systems and systematic monitoring of controlled prototypes.

Evolution of strategic research for the savannas: from monocropping to integrated crop-livestock systems

About 1989, strategic research on savannas took a new direction when the CIAT Rice and Tropical Pasture

Programs began to develop the concept of agropastoral systems for the Colombian savannas (Zeigler et al. 1993). This approach took well-proven and adapted pasture technologies in the ecosystem and combined them with CIAT's newly developed, acid-tolerant, upland rice lines. The object was to intensify and diversify land use by generating cash (through rice production) needed for improved pasture establishment and renovation. CIAT established its first agropastoral systems trials at Matazul in 1989, combining these newly released varieties with exotic, adapted, forage-grass species, with and without legumes.

In Brazil, EMBRAPA had earlier tested the system with less well-adapted rice and forage grasses without legumes. These evaluations were usually researcher-managed, on-farm trials in which infrastructure and logistics allowed only basic observations of production and soil analysis. More systematic, process-oriented research on agropastoral and crop rotational systems began in Brazil in 1991 and in Colombia in 1993. The Brazilian research began by establishing systems experiments on long-term, crop rotation/ley pasture at EMBRAPA's Centro de Pesquisa Agropecuária dos Cerrados (CPAC) station at Planaltina. The same type of research was conducted in Colombia at the Centro Nacional de Investigación (CNI) at Carimagua. The long-term experiment at Carimagua was supported with satellite experiments that were designed to quantify specific biophysical processes, particularly N and P dynamics.

In the Matazul area, on-farm evaluation of alternatives progressed from agropastoral systems based on rice to other pioneer crops such as maize and soybeans, which were used to establish pastures with higher nutrient demand such as *Panicum*

maximum. Simultaneously, contrasting land uses on the well-drained savannas were monitored on farm. These assessed how alternative management practices affected the evolution of natural resources and agricultural productivity and identified soil properties for potential use as SQIs.

In 1992, on-farm activities began in Uberlândia, Brazil, to develop improved legume-based agropastoral systems for the *Cerrados*. Because the *Cerrados* are more agriculturally developed than other savanna areas, how changes in land use improved or degraded soil could be analyzed cross-sectionally. One farm (Fazenda Sta. Terezhina) on fragile sandy soils had records, going back for more than 10 years, on inputs, outputs, and land management. The farm had been transformed from a traditional, extensive cattle ranch to an integrated, agropastoral operation with regular rotations of crops with pastures.

Initially, strategic research on systems on the savannas was supply driven, particularly in the Colombian *Llanos*. Here, agriculture remains at a low intensity and is mostly in transition from extensive cattle ranching on native pastures to sowing of improved exotic grasses. Agricultural systems development in the *Cerrados* has a longer history of transition, encouraged by better infrastructure and subsidies. It has often progressed along the development path shown in Figure 1, ahead of researcher innovation and evaluation.

Natural resource management programs initially lacked input from a resource economist. In the *Llanos*, this input may well have differently emphasized systems research. Expectations are that the development path of the *Llanos* will follow that of the *Cerrados*, although perhaps over more time than anticipated

(Smith et al. 1997). In this sense, the strategy was to assess the consequences of the *Cerrados* experience and evaluate how alternative systems affected the soil resource and sustainable production. In Brazil, a resource economist collaborated on the dynamics of land use. This led to more emphasis on characterizing land-use dynamics and degradation problems on small dairy farms.

Problems encountered during research

Biophysical strategic research in the savannas of Brazil and Colombia has focused on two long-term systems experiments at Planaltina and Carimagua. Both encountered similar problems. First, these types of experiments are demanding in human and capital resources, and require a long-term commitment not easily obtained in the present funding environment. At Carimagua, the effects of contrasting systems on soil quality or of alternative management strategies on recuperating degraded systems and maintaining sustainable ones could not be fully evaluated because of reduced resources and logistical problems.

In Brazil, a frequent problem was lack of seed of promising legumes (cv. Mineirão and *Arachis* sp.) to validate results on a larger scale. Farmers were key in solving the problem: once convinced of its value, they spent their own resources to multiply seed. In 1996, a farmer planted 40 ha of 'Mineirão' and harvested 1 ton of seed, compared with the preceding 4 years of work, during which only a little more than 200 kg of *Stylosanthes guianensis* cv. Mineirão and *Arachis pintoi* were produced. This seed was used to expand testing of the prototypes within the same region and to other areas and production

systems (e.g., Mato Grosso and Tocantins).

Also difficult was obtaining seed for the on-station systems experiment at Carimagua. In 1993, establishing high-input systems was delayed because of insufficient acid-tolerant maize seed from the Centro Internacional de Mejoramiento de Maíz y Trigo (CIMMYT). Moreover, problems occurred in obtaining high-quality *Panicum maximum* seed for the pastures to be sown under maize.

Both long-term experiments also had difficulty in maintaining the participation of national partners because of financial and other problems. At Carimagua, a multidisciplinary CIAT team led the long-term experiment. Although interest was high at the institutional level, it was difficult for CORPOICA to keep a team of scientists at Carimagua to ensure enduring participation in the experiment. Further, the failure to involve national scientists in the planning stages probably resulted in a reduced sense of ownership of (and perhaps commitment to) the experiment.

Control over on-farm experiments is a perennial problem. Losing information, treatments, and results through misunderstandings and lack of care by inexperienced workers is always a risk. Also, the long-term commitment to a particular crop, system, or management practice in prototypes cannot be guaranteed, especially if these are unprofitable or clearly degrading. The farmer may then be averse to continuing, even though longer-term observations may be required to capture the effects or quantify the processes under study.

In the *Cerrados* (Uberlândia), farmers participated in most stages of the on-farm research, including evaluation of forage components for improved agropastoral systems and evaluation of prototypes. They did not, however, participate in the management of the experiments. On the *Llanos* (Colombia), initial "best-bet" agropastoral trials were planted at Matazul, close to the main trunk road. This generated considerable interest amongst graziers and, particularly, amongst "immigrants" from other parts of the country. A result was that substantial areas of pastures were renovated through the use of introduced, improved pasture and crop-pasture technologies developed by CIAT and its partners.

Results: Successes and Failures

Examples of results of CIAT's strategic research in systems are presented here in four thematic areas. Successes are considered both in terms of farmer adoption of technologies and in the development of tools for measuring the current and predicting the future impact of systems on soil resources and the environment.

Introducing and evaluating new systems and components

The agropastoral technology for pasture establishment and renovation

has been among the most significant outputs of systems research in the savannas. Although EMBRAPA had already demonstrated some biophysical and economic benefits of the agropastoral technology for the *Cerrados*, the system was unknown in the Colombian *Llanos* when it was tested. In Brazil, the system was based on use of high inputs made possible in part by the availability of lime deposits; legumes usually were not part of the system. On the Colombian *Llanos*, low inputs, often only of P without maintenance applications, contributed to rapid degeneration of improved pastures and poor persistence of legumes, where sown.

CIAT's innovation was to combine acid-tolerant rice germplasm with forage grasses and legumes in systems that did not require high inputs of lime or nutrients (Vera et al. 1992). With the acid-tolerant rice varieties, the agropastoral system also became possible in the *Llanos* where, unlike in the *Cerrados*, no lime deposits exist.

The first on-farm trials at Matazul showed that *Brachiaria dictyoneura* + *Centrosema acutifolium,* and *Andropogon gayanus* + *Stylosanthes capitata* pastures, sown under rice, established and were ready for grazing sooner than when sown alone with conventional low rates of inputs. Rice yields were unaffected by competition

Table 2. Comparison of production of rice and pasture establishment in agropastoral systems at the Matazul Farm, Department of Meta, Colombia, 1989.

System	Production[a] (kg/ha dry matter)			
	Rice grain	Grass	Legume	Weeds
Rice monoculture	2230 a	-	-	650 a
Rice + pastures[b]	2090 a	1220 a	210 b	670 a
Rice + pastures[c]	1960 a	1770 a	440 a	430 a

a. Values within a column followed by the same letter are not significantly different.
b. *Brachiaria dictyoneura* + *Centrosema acutifolium.*
c. *Andropogon gayanus* + *Stylosanthes capitata.*
SOURCE: CIAT 1991b.

from the pastures (Table 2). During 1989-1992, the agronomy of this system on the *Llanos* was worked out. Trials were carried out to establish the effects of timing and type of land preparation, seeding rates and density of rice and pastures and their relative dates of planting, and the nutrient requirements of the system. Establishment (on native savanna) and renovation of degraded pastures among other pasture species were also evaluated. The returns on the sale of rice were more than enough to offset the costs of rice and forage seed and inputs. Thus, the technology was considered an attractive means of pasture establishment and renovation for graziers (Vera et al. 1992).

A main aim of the Brazilian project was to develop agropastoral systems based on multipurpose legumes. Germplasm evaluation identified *S. guianensis* cv. Mineirão as a potential component of legume-based, agropastoral systems with low use of inputs on both clayey and sandy soils. Animal liveweight gains increased by more than 50% in the rice-grass-legume associations, compared with the rice-grass systems (Table 3); and milk production increased by 15%-30% in systems that included 'Mineirão' (data not shown). However, crop components other than rice were lacking for low-input agropastoral systems. Comparisons of rice undersown with 'Mineirão' and three different grasses, both simultaneously or 30 days apart, showed the competitive effects of grasses on rice yields and legume establishment and indicated means of reducing it (delayed sowing). Similar evaluations of pasture establishment under maize with high inputs were also carried out. Although evaluations of *Arachis pintoi* BRA-031143 in high-input systems were also successful (results not shown), the project was unable to identify other legumes better adapted for high-input systems.

Effects of systems on soil quality; identifying SQIs

Agricultural systems can have both adverse and ameliorative effects on the soil. Examination of the soils' physical, chemical, and biological properties in the *Llanos* and *Cerrados* has demonstrated strong positive effects of integrating crops and pastures in agropastoral systems. At the Matazul Farm, in the systems experiments, soil aggregation was maintained or enhanced, and soil bulk density reduced, under improved pastures (Table 4). Earthworm biomass was increased, whereas that of termites was reduced under renovated pasture, and both microbial biomass N and P

Table 3. Animal liveweight gain (LWG) in agropastoral prototypes sown in two production systems and two soil types in Uberlândia, Brazil.

Production system	Input use	Soil type	Annual animal production (kg/ha LWG)		Production increase with legumes (%)
			I[a]	II[b]	
Pastures	Low	Sandy	160	254	58
Pastures	Low	Clayey	230	354	54
Crops	High	Sandy	236	267	10

a. Crop + grass.
b. Crop + grass + legume.
SOURCE: CIAT 1997.

Table 4. Soil quality parameters in a savanna Oxisol under different long-term prototype systems at the Matazul Farm, Department of Meta, Colombia, 1995.

System (%)	Soil aggregation in top 2.5 cm of soil			Bulk density of top 12.5 cm of soil (g/cm³)	Macrofauna biomass in top 30 cm of soil (g/cm³)		Microbial biomass (µg/g)	
	>4 mm	1-4 mm	<1 mm		Earthworms	Termites	N	P
Savanna	38	28	35	1.4	3.4	2.4	53	9.6
Degraded pasture[a]	25	32	44	1.3	3.9	7.1	-	-
Renovated pasture[b]	32	30	38	1.3	6.0	2.2	62	12.8
Rice monoculture[c]	14	30	57	1.3	1.5	1.9	34	9.8

a. *Brachiaria dictyoneura* + legumes established with rice in 1989.
b. *B. dictyoneura* + legumes established with rice in 1989 and renovated with rice in 1993.
c. Continuous since 1989.

SOURCE: CIAT 1995b.

were increased, indicating a higher level of nutrient cycling in the renovated pasture system. Conversely, soil under continuous rice suffered loss of aggregation and reduced macro- and microbiological activity.

Similar observations were made for the *Cerrados*. Cross-sectional analyses were used in on-farm studies in Uberlândia, Brazil, where potential SQIs were compared in sandy and clayey Oxisols with relatively long histories (>12 years). These farms had had different systems of land use, including cultivated crops, pastures, reforestation, and native savanna. Several microbiological parameters were found to be more sensitive to soil-quality changes than to total soil C (Table 5). Reduced values of microbial biomass C, the proportion of microbial C in total soil organic C, and enzymatic activities indicated by dimethyl sulfoxide (DMSO) and ρ-nitrophenol reduction (phosphatase) were associated with more intense cropping. Examination of P fractionation in these systems found that applied P accumulated primarily in labile (Olsen NaHCO$_3$ extractable) and moderately labile (NaOH extractable) pools and entered organic pools only in heavier soils that

supported a higher level of microbial and biological activity.

Similar observations made at the Carimagua Station found that short-term (1-4 y) fluxes of P moved primarily into labile inorganic pools under the spectrum of systems (continuous cropping to improved pastures, Friesen et al. 1997). Studies of long-term (16-y-old) *Brachiaria* pastures at Carimagua found that applied P partitioned between inorganic and organic P pools in proportions similar to those of native soil P (CIAT 1995a). Failure of P to enter organic pools is thought to indicate a degrading system, suggesting a low level of P cycling in the system (Stewart and Tiessen 1987).

Studies of soil aggregation in Uberlândia found that macroaggregates were more sensitive to land-use changes than other aggregate sizes, and that sandy soils were more susceptible than clayey soils (results not shown). A cross-sectional study on sandy loam soils on the Fazenda Sta. Terezhina Farm demonstrated the effects of continuous cropping on loss of soil structure, and the recuperating effects of pastures (Figure 4). Comparisons of aggregate

Table 5. Potential soil quality indicators identified in cross-sectional studies in Uberlândia, Brazil[a].

Land use	Total soil C (µg/g soil)	Microbial C (µg/g soil)	C_{mic}/C[b] (%)	DMSO[c] reduction (µg/g soil per ha)	Phosphate activity[d] (µg of NP/g soil per ha)	Olsen[e]		NaOH[e]	
						P_i	P_o	P_i	P_o
Loamy Oxisol									
Savanna	22.7 abc	730	3.2 c	0.7 ab	549 ab	2.5 a	3.3 a	14 a	24 a
Pasture	25.0 c	753	2.9 bc	1.0 bc	911 c	3.2 a	2.1 a	15 a	29 a
Reforestation	20.8 ab	538	2.2 ab	0.5 a	406 a	5.6 a	5.1 a	27 b	33 a
Crops	21.2 abc	470	2.1 a	0.5 a	425 a	15.0 b	3.1 a	53 c	40 a
Clayey Oxisol									
Savanna	8.9 ab	465	5.3	0.6	343 b	4.3 a	6.2 a	33 a	66 a
Pasture	9.9 b	406	4.4	0.3	338 b	4.6 a	4.4 a	33 a	82 ab
Reforestation	-	-	-	-	-	5.8 a	6.2 ab	49 a	90 b
Crops	8.0 a	252	3.2	0.3	245 a	14.0 b	8.6 b	95 b	100 b

a. On a given soil type, land-use systems followed by the same letters are not significantly different.
b. C_{mic}/C = proportion of microbial carbon in total organic carbon.
c. DMSO = dimethyl sulfoxide.
d. NP = ρ-nitrophenol.
e. P_i = inorganic P; P_o = organic P; both are measured in µg of P/g soil.
SOURCE: CIAT 1997.

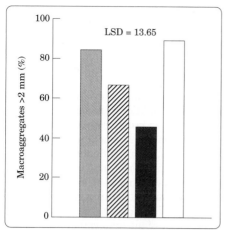

Figure 4.   Effect of soil management on the proportion of macroaggregates in a sandy loam in Uberlândia, Brazil. (▨ = *Cerrados*; ▨ = cropped 1 year; ■ = cropped 4 years; ▢ = crop/pasture.) (Taken from CIAT 1997.)

Preliminary results showed macroaggregate contents to be highly correlated with SOM and sand content (Figure 5).

Although such parameters show sensitivity to declining soil quality, to serve as SQIs, changes must be correlated with reduced productivity and/or increased environmental degradation. Further, to be of diagnostic value, they need to be evaluated across a much wider range of soil types and systems to establish critical thresholds. As indicated earlier, finding a sufficiently wide range of land uses while maintaining control of confounding variables impedes the application of cross-sectional analysis to define SQI thresholds.

size distribution in light and heavy soils under native savanna, traditional pasture, and crop/pasture systems found intensified land use resulted in declines in macroaggregate contents, which were also associated with reduced SOM content. A range of land-use types was extensively sampled in different landscapes in the Colombian well-drained savannas.

The consensus of the *Cerrados* experience is that cross-sectional analysis enabled SQIs to be generated relatively quickly. Results from those and other studies, however, are open to criticism for lack of replication and the effects of spatial heterogeneity on their interpretation. Nonetheless, the alternative of establishing the requisite range in controlled experiments could be prohibitive both in time and cost.

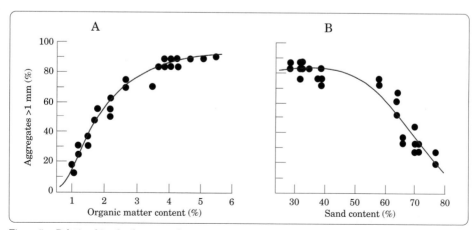

Figure 5.   Relationship of soil content of macroaggregates (>1 mm) with (A) soil organic matter content, and with (B) soil sand content on farms under different land uses and in different landscapes in the Colombian savannas (taken from CIAT 1997).

The systems trials at Matazul and the process-oriented experiments at Carimagua and Planaltina have a limited range of treatments but permit observing the dynamics of change under controlled conditions. The trials provide a platform for studying and quantifying soil processes. Simulation models can be developed and calibrated to evaluate the effects of changes in systems and their management on the natural resource base.

Understanding and quantifying systems processes

Research on plant and soil processes has focused primarily on the cycling of N and P in systems. The dynamics of earthworm populations were also studied in systems. We present results of studies of the cycling of N in rotational systems as an example of CIAT's strategic research on soil-plant processes (Friesen et al. 1997).

Studies on key N-cycling processes included N uptake from soil and recovery from crop/forage residues, rates of mineral N leaching through soil profiles, factors affecting water dynamics in the soil profile, and the interaction of mineral N ions with the mineral complex. Nitrogen release rates have been quantified for a wide selection of plant materials under field conditions, using the "litterbag" methodology. Grain legume residues and green manures were found to decompose rapidly in soil, releasing (in the case of soybean residues, Figure 6)

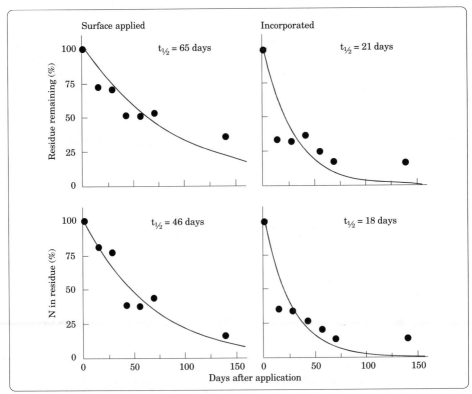

Figure 6. Rates of decomposition and N release from soybean residues applied to the surface or incorporated into 5 cm in an Oxisol at Carimagua, Colombia ($t_{1/2}$ = time required to release 50% of N content). (CIAT, unpublished results.)

50% of their N content within 3 weeks of incorporation.

Measurements of mineral N in soil profiles under various systems (Figure 7) showed substantial nitrate production and its movement down through the soil profile in the early rainy season before crop roots are established and able to capture it. Strategies are needed to improve nutrient use efficiency and avoid groundwater and environmental contamination. Some possibilities are improving synchronization of N release with plant demand; using catch crops, or cover or relay crops; or managing residues to reduce decomposition rates and increase the capture of mineralized N.

Results of such process studies depend highly on interactions among local environmental conditions (and soil characteristics) and crops, and include both crop production and impact of systems on the environment. Simulation models can integrate the effects of interacting processes and soil and climatic variables, and can reduce the site specificity inherent in NRM research. Thus, process studies have been conducted, together with the assembly of minimum data sets needed for models such as the Decision Support System for Agrotechnology Transfer (DSSAT) family of crop simulation models (Tsuji et al. 1994).

In testing the rice/green manure system, the DSSAT N submodel underpredicted nitrate concentrations in the soil profile in a time-series of samplings (Figure 7). This may be because it underestimated nitrate retention by the surface soil, or N

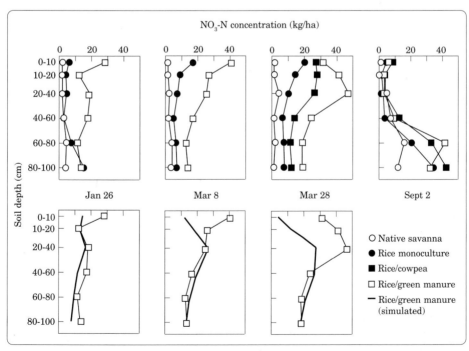

Figure 7.   Nitrate content in soil profiles under different systems at four samplings in 1974: early dry (Jan 26), mid-dry (Mar 8), early rainy (Mar 28), and mid-rainy (Sept 2) seasons. Upper-tier graphs present observed nitrate profiles; lower-tier graphs present observed and simulated profiles under the rice/green manure system during the dry season (Jan 26-Mar 28). Green manure was incorporated in late November, 1993. (Adapted from Friesen et al. 1998.)

production from decomposing green manure, or both. Increased understanding and quantifying the processes affecting soil nitrate concentrations and movement is needed to better predict the environmental consequences of green manures and enable testing of alternative components and methods of management to mitigate nitrate leaching.

Research on soil-plant processes is usually highly sample intensive, requires sufficient infrastructure and capital resources to manage the samples, and needs careful supervision of methodologies to obtain reliable and reproducible results. Despite Carimagua's remote location, the existing infrastructure made it a logical site for process studies and for establishing long-term crop rotations/ley pastures experiments. However, careful supervision of methods has occasionally been problematical. Reduced transport options have further exacerbated this and complicated the management of samples, particularly those that must be processed fresh.

Although the application of crop simulation models has been the ultimate focus of process-oriented research, lack of in-house expertise has limited progress. Currently, work is being carried out largely through collaborative arrangements with other institutions. Lack of formal arrangements (e.g., through joint-funded projects), however, reduces this activity's priority with collaborators, particularly when they are highly committed to other projects.

Identifying socioeconomic driving forces behind land-use change

At present, infrastructure is improving only gradually in the Colombian *Llanos*; land prices are increasing; and

capital gains from land investments are tending to outweigh profits from technological advances. Nonetheless, adopting improved pastures on small areas is profitable. By 1995, about 20% of the total area had been planted mainly to improved grasses, compared with 0% in 1979. This is probably because animal liveweight gains per ha can be increased by more than 16 times on improved grasses, compared with grazing on native savanna; that is, by three times overall when production is weighted for the actual area improved (Smith et al. 1997). Once land prices reach a plateau, farmers will, theoretically, be more interested in available technological innovations, such as ley-farming or crop/pasture systems, that would be more appropriate for this phase of the development path rather than when land prices are rapidly increasing.

In Brazil, during the last 20-30 years, expansion in the *Cerrados* has slowed considerably as subsidies were removed and grains such as soybeans became less profitable. These factors led to a decline of more than 20% in land prices in 1995, thus reducing incentives for frontier expansion (Smith et al. ndb). Landowners have become increasingly interested in technological options that improve production and the efficiency of inputs used. Modeling has indicated that both policy and technological advances are required to improve production and to avoid increasing off-site problems such as water pollution and silting (Smith et al. ndb). A study of the adoption of an NRM-conserving technology (no-till cropping systems) showed that, contrary to popular belief, financial stress can stimulate adoption (Smith et al. nda). Farmers are adopting the "no-till" technology, despite recognizing that it does not appear to offer short-term economic advantages. Reasons for adoption include labor savings, reduced fuel consumption, alleviation of major soil constraints (e.g., reduced soil moisture, erosion, and compaction), and ease of management. The private sector has played a large role in promoting the technology, although its interest may rest more in agrochemical sales (herbicides in particular) than in soil conservation per se.

Socioeconomic and land-use modeling studies of systems suggest that technology, land speculation, and characteristics of the natural resource base interact in complex ways to determine both the nature and rate of intensification (Smith et al. 1997). Furthermore, they suggest that a better understanding of these interactions is needed to accurately focus strategic research on the development of technological options.

Conclusions: Lessons Learned

Natural resource management research should include a mix of on-station and on-farm activities. In the savannas, these have been balanced, although farmer participatory research has been greater in the *Cerrados* than the *Llanos* (in part because the *Cerrados* are more populated and landowners there also tend to be operators). Cross-sectional studies and opportunistic measurements at the farm level are perhaps the fastest way to assess long-term effects of conventional and improved systems. But, they are of little help in assessing the impact of innovative technologies that have no history of on-farm use.

A criticism of NRM research continues to be that it is site specific. For this reason, research must focus on principles and processes so to extrapolate findings. Thus, both on-farm research (to assess new technologies) and controlled on-station experimentation are needed. However, they must be better related to the demand-driven issues of natural resource use that emerge from such research as on-farm fieldwork, socioeconomic characterization, and feedback and interaction between scientists and farmers involved in participatory research.

Evaluating crop and pasture at the farm level, especially in small plots, is a problem because farmers have neither the time for, nor the interest in, work at this scale. A better alternative is to establish farmer-conducted trials on scales closer to their systems. In the *Cerrados*, farmers are more familiar with crops and crop research than with pasture research, making it more difficult to do experiments with forages. In both the *Cerrados* and *Llanos*, livestock producers have neither interest nor experience in cropping. Thus, farmers from other parts of Colombia who have had this experience have been the main adopters of the agropastoral technology developed on the *Llanos*.

The experience in Brazil has shown that research with the more dynamic farmers is important for identifying resource-use problems, capturing farmers' perceptions, and developing potential solutions. For example, close interaction with one farmer resulted in the evaluation of several chemical and mechanical methods for controlling competition of the *Arachis pintoi* cover crop with annual crops sown into it. In another case, the farmer ran satellite experiments to test his solution. Other advantages of farmer involvement were reduced operational costs for managing improved prototypes because their establishment was done with farmer resources (e.g., machinery, fertilizers, animals, fencing) and assistance with producing seed of promising materials.

Although interaction with farmers has been relatively successful, participatory methodologies have not been formally applied. Biophysical scientists are only now familiarizing themselves with participatory research methods. A wider suite of disciplines is needed in interdisciplinary teams to speed up the development and adoption of new technologies, especially where intensification is occurring (e.g., the small-farm sector in the Brazilian *Cerrados*).

On-farm research is complex and, in some cases, difficult to conduct if one follows a reductionist approach. A holistic, multidisciplinary, and multi-institutional approach, based on demand-driven objectives and goals, needs to be adopted. Basic and applied research has to be integrated to achieve impact in the short term. Previously, biophysical scientists working in the savannas sought to develop principles and understand processes under controlled conditions, using a reductionist approach. The challenge now is to find ways of developing effective farmer participation in strategic research on NRM at the farm, watershed, or regional levels. Although the savannas were well characterized at the outset, use of socioeconomic analysis to develop objectives for strategic research would have strengthened the relationship between mechanistic and applied on-farm research and perhaps would have resulted in a different focus.

Acknowledgments

The development of a strategic research agenda on production systems for the South American savannas was based on the intellectual contributions of a great many former colleagues, among them being R. Vera, J. Toledo, M. Fisher, I. M. Rao, C. Lascano, J. Spain, and P. Kerridge, whose assistance we gratefully acknowledge.

References

Bourlag NE; Dowswell CR. 1994. Feeding a human population that increasingly crowds a fragile planet. Keynote lecture. 15th World Congress of Soil Science, July 10-16, 1994, Acapulco, Mexico. 15 p. (Supplement to transactions.)

CIAT. 1991a. CIAT in the 1990s and beyond: a strategic plan. Cali, Colombia. 125 p. (Includes Supplement.)

CIAT. 1991b. Tropical Pastures Program annual report 1987-91, vol 2. Cali, Colombia. 558 p.

CIAT. 1994. Savannas Program biennial report 1992-1993. Working document no. 134. Cali, Colombia. 125 p.

CIAT. 1995a. Tropical Lowlands Program annual report 1994. Working document no. 148. Cali, Colombia. 258 p.

CIAT. 1995b. Tropical Lowlands Program annual report 1995. Working document no. 151. Cali, Colombia. 60 p.

CIAT. 1997. Annual report of Project PE-2: Confronting Soil Degradation. Cali, Colombia. 124 p.

Friesen D; Rao IM; Thomas RJ; Oberson A; Sanz JI. 1997. Phosphorus acquisition and cycling in crop and pasture systems in low fertility tropical soils. Plant Soil 196:289-294.

Friesen D; Thomas RJ; Rivera A; Asakawa N; Bowen W. 1998. Nitrogen dynamics under monocultures and crop rotations on a Colombian savannas Oxisol. Paper presented at the 16th World Congress of Soil Science, 20-26 Aug 1998, Montpellier, France.

Jones PG; Robison DM; Carter SE. 1991. A GIS approach to identifying research problems and opportunities in natural resource management. In: CIAT in the 1990s and beyond, a strategic plan: supplement. CIAT, Cali, Colombia. p 73-110.

Parton WJ; Stewart JWB; Cole CV. 1988. Dynamics of C, N, P, and S in grassland soils: a model. Biogeochemistry (Dordr) 5:109-131.

Parton WJ; Woomer PL; Martin A. 1994. Modelling soil organic matter dynamics and plant productivity in tropical ecosystems. In: Woomer PL; Swift MJ, eds. The biological management of tropical soil fertility. John Wiley, London. p 171-188.

Sanint LR; Seré CO; Rivas L; Ramírez A. 1992. The savannas of South America: towards a research agenda for CIAT. In: Trends in CIAT commodities 1992. Working document no. 111. CIAT, Cali, Colombia. p 149-179.

Smith J; Cadavid JV; Rincón A; Vera R. 1997. Land speculation and intensification at the frontier: a seeming paradox in the Colombian savanna. Agric Sys 54:501-520.

Smith J; Cadavid JV; Ayarza M; Pimenta de Aguiar JL. nda. Adoption of resource management technologies: lessons learned from the Brazilian savanna. J Sust Agric (in press).

Smith J; Winograd M; Gallopín G; Pachico D. ndb. Dynamics of the agricultural frontier in the Amazon and savannas of Brazil: analyzing the impact of policy and technology. Environ Model Develop (in press).

Stewart JWB; Tiessen H. 1987. Dynamics of soil organic phosphorus. Biogeochemistry (Dordr) 4:41-60.

TAC (Technical Advisory Committee). 1992. A CGIAR response to UNCED Agenda 21 recommendations. TAC Secretariat of the Consultative Group on International Agricultural Research and Food and Agriculture Organization of the United Nations (FAO), Rome.

Tsuji GY; Uehra G; Balas S, eds. 1994. DSSATv3, 3 vols. University of Hawaii, Honolulu. (Guide included.)

UNCED (United Nations Conference on Environment and Development). 1992. The global partnership for environment and development: a guide to Agenda 21. Geneva, Switzerland. 116 p.

Vera R; Thomas RJ; Sanint LR; Sanz JI. 1992. Development of sustainable ley-farming systems for the acid-soil savannas of tropical America. An Acad Bras Cienc 64:105-125.

Zeigler RS; Sanz JI; Toledo JM. 1993. Developing sustainable agricultural production systems for the acid savannas of Latin America. In: Paoletti MG; Napier TL; Ferro O; Stinner BR; Stinner D, eds. Socio-economic and policy issues for sustainable farming systems. Cooperativa Amicizia, Padova, Italy. p 103-116.

CHAPTER 5

Developing Improved Pasture Systems for Forest Margins

C. Lascano*, G. Ruiz*, J. Velásquez**,
J. Rozo***, and M. Jervis***

Introduction

The value of pastures for a livestock producer depends largely on the pastures' capacity to produce animal products, which, in turn, is related to the quantity and quality of the forage on offer. In tropical regions such as forest margins, liveweight gain and milk yield can be significantly depressed in pastures of grass alone (Toledo 1985). Grass pastures sown in areas with low soil fertility degrade over time if no fertilizer is applied or if the species used are susceptible to prevailing pests (e.g., spittlebug). Such degradation is partly reflected by loss of grass productivity and weed invasion, which then affect the pastures' carrying capacity and thus animal performance.

The use of legumes in pastures is one way of minimizing short- and long-term declines in quality and quantity of forage biomass and thus of increasing livestock production (Lascano and Avila 1991; Lascano and Estrada 1989). The rationale for this alternative is that tropical legumes have a higher nutritive value than grasses and, through symbiotic

nitrogen fixation, can enhance production and quality of the companion grass and improve soil fertility. However, in tropical America, incorporating legumes into pasture systems in marginal areas is slow, partly because farmers are unaware of the potential benefits of this technology (Toledo and Nores 1986). A major effort is thus needed to show the livestock farming community how legumes can increase beef and milk production and to advise on pasture management.

Below, we summarize experiences with an on-farm project aimed at recuperating degraded pastures by using legumes on dual-purpose cattle farms established in a region of forest margins in the Colombian Amazon.

Targeted Area

The Colombian Department of Caquetá (about 0° to 2° N and about 71° to 76° W) is characterized by acid soils and high rainfall (3200 mm/y). An integral part of the South American tropical rain forest that forms the Amazon Basin, Caquetá covers 8.9 million hectares, including about 6.6 million hectares of rain forest and 1.8 million hectares of Andean piedmont. Of the latter, 1.4 million hectares are estimated as being below

*   CIAT, Cali, Colombia.
**   Corporación Colombiana de Investigación
     Agropecuaria (CORPOICA)—Macagual.
*** Nestlé de Colombia, S.A.

1000 masl. The land is dedicated to cattle raising, and 90% of Caquetá's population is found in the piedmont region.

Over the last 40 years, the area around the capital city of Florencia has been subject to an intensive process of colonization. Consequently, an estimated 1 million hectares have been totally deforested, with much of this area covered by unproductive naturalized grasses or degraded introduced grasses of the genus *Brachiaria*, dedicated to dual-purpose cattle raising (Ramírez and Seré 1990). Good markets for beef and milk favor this type of semi-intensive system (Michelsen 1990). The Caquetá piedmont region produces about 57 million liters of milk per year, which represent about 2% of the total production in Colombia.

Objectives and Institutional Relationships

Project objectives

The project's overall goal was to help increase farmers' incomes and milk production for urban consumers by promoting the use of appropriate forage-based technologies that not only are more productive but also help conserve the natural resource base. To accomplish this goal, the project focused on reclaiming degraded pastures by introducing legumes, well-known for improving forage quality and enhancing nutrient cycling. The specific objectives of the 4-year project were to:

1. Document the on-farm benefits of *Arachis*-based pastures;

2. Train personnel of different institutions how to establish and use *Arachis*-based pastures

through participatory methods; and

3. Initiate and catalyze an active transfer mechanism of the *Arachis* technology in the region.

Project background

During 1987 to 1990, CIAT's forage researchers collaborated with several institutions present in the region to select grass and legume germplasm adapted to acid soils and with a potential for reclaiming degraded pastures. Some studies also examined techniques for establishing grass/legume pastures using minimum tillage. This initial effort resulted in identifying grasses and legumes of high quality and productivity. The most successful pasture was a legume/grass association of *Arachis pintoi* grown with several *Brachiaria* species. This was not surprising, given that *Arachis pintoi* exhibits high nutritional quality (Lascano and Thomas 1988), compatibility with aggressive grasses (Grof 1985), and persistence under grazing (Lascano 1994), even in acid soils under humid savanna conditions. Limited on-farm evaluation of *Arachis*-based pastures indicated that it persists under all types of farmer management.

Livestock producers in the region, however, were not adopting the *Arachis* technology, the main reasons being lack of promotion, ignorance of benefits, and high cost of seed. Nestlé de Colombia, S.A. (a private institution) was approached for funding to enable CIAT to coordinate an on-farm research and development (R&D) program and work in cooperation with the Corporación Colombiana de Investigación Agropecuaria (CORPOICA) and the Universidad de la Amazonia (both public institutions). The aim was to increase milk production by reclaiming degraded pastures in the piedmont region of Caquetá.

prices of *Arachis* seed in the market limited its adoption by farmers.

Problems Addressed and Beneficiaries

Problems

Previous diagnostic studies carried out in the region had identified the potential of and constraints to increasing milk production in the piedmont region of Caquetá (Michelsen 1990; Ramírez and Seré 1990; Ulrich et al. 1994). These studies showed that, despite the existence of a good market for fresh milk (i.e., Nestlé plants), milk production per dual-purpose cow (3-4 L/day) and per unit area (600-700 L/ha) was low because of the following factors:

1. Native pastures (i.e., *Homolepsis aturensis, Paspalum* spp.), which have a low carrying capacity, cover a high proportion of the grazing area;

2. A high proportion of introduced grasses (i.e., *Brachiaria decumbens*) were degraded because of heavy and continuous spittlebug attacks, lack of maintenance and fertilization, and inadequate grazing management; and

3. The breed of milking cows used (Zebu-based) has a low genetic potential for producing milk; neither did farmers select heavily for this trait.

Subsequent data collected indicated that, despite the positive demonstrations given at the farm of the Fondo Ganadero del Valle on the use of *Arachis*-based pastures, the adoption of this and other well-adapted herbaceous legumes was extremely low. The low availability and high

Beneficiaries

An Advisory Committee for the project was formed to define its modus operandi. Committee members were representatives of the participating institutions, with the CIAT representative as chairman. Criteria for selecting farmers were discussed at the Advisory Committee first meeting. Farmers who were to participate in the project had to:

1. Exhibit some leadership among other livestock farmers in the region;

2. Want to recuperate degraded pastures on the farm and have the economic means to contribute to the establishment of grass and grass/legume pastures that were large enough to hold a milking herd for a minimum of 1 week to allow unbiased estimates of milk yield;

3. Have a farm with easy access by road at all times of the year;

4. Sell milk produced on the farm to Nestlé;

5. Permit data collection (i.e., botanical composition of pastures and daily milk yields) from the experimental pastures; and

6. Authorize other farmers to visit the farm during programmed field days.

Based on the above criteria, the project's main beneficiaries were medium-scale cattle producers, who did not derive their income exclusively from livestock farming. However, these farmers wished to increase milk yield and realized that a major constraint to achieving this goal was poor cow nutrition caused by the low quantity and quality of edible biomass in degraded pastures.

Research Methods Used

On all the farms participating in the project, two types of pastures would be established: grass alone, and grass associated with commercial *Arachis* (cv. Maní Forrajero). Newly established pastures were to be grazed mainly by the milking herd and to form part of the normal paddock rotation practiced on the farm, using the methodology proposed by Lascano et al. (1997).

Pasture measurements, including forage on offer and botanical composition (using BOTANAL; Tothill et al. 1978), were to be taken three or four times a year on each farm. Milk yield of individual cows was to be measured on each farm at least four times a year. The farm manager was to measure daily bulk milk from the experimental pastures two to three times per week.

Other measurements such as soil chemical fertility, soil physical structure, and soil biological activity would be taken once a year by the project's technical assistants (TAs).

Project Development

The project is now 3 years old. Some planned and unplanned activities are described below.

Planned activities

The project's main activity was to establish 102 ha of grass alone and in mixture with *Arachis* on 16 farms. The size of paddocks ranged from 2 to 15 ha. The experimental pastures were periodically monitored in terms of botanical composition and milk yield.

Other planned activities carried out were:

1. Establishing new ecotypes of *Arachis* for distribution of vegetative seed;

2. Studying alternative methods of land preparation;

3. Studying fertilization for establishing *Arachis*;

4. Holding field days to demonstrate successes and failures in establishing *Arachis* and to show results of milk production;

5. Publishing technical bulletins and newsletters; and

6. Giving short courses for TAs on the *Arachis* technology; its uses and benefits; and methods of measuring soil physical properties, root length and distribution in pasture components, and soil biological activity (earthworms).

The project was to rely on participatory methods for transferring technology, that is, farmers were to be directly involved, providing the necessary feedback to researchers and TAs for modifying the technology being promoted and easing its adoption. Given this basic philosophy, a one-week's training course on participatory research (PR) was offered to TAs participating in the project and other TAs chosen by R&D institutions present in the region. Course topics included:

1. A conceptual basis of participatory methods;

2. Techniques and practice on how to interview farmers;

3. Techniques and practice on how to involve farmers in selecting new grasses and legumes from agronomic plots;

4. A video of all practical aspects covered in the course; and

5. A list of common terms used by livestock managers in the region.

Unplanned activities

As the project progressed, it became clear that the commercial cultivar of *A. pintoi* (cv. Maní Forrajero; Rincón et al. 1992) was not adapted to the less fertile soils found in the rolling hills (*mesones*) that comprised 60% of the project's area of influence. Evidence came from small-plot evaluation trials of different ecotypes of *Arachis* in association with a grass and managed under grazing. In these evaluations, the commercial *Arachis* did not persist for more than 2 years. Consequently, planting in the *mesones* needed to be delayed until sufficient seed of new *Arachis* ecotypes was available for large-scale planting.

Informal surveys also indicated that some farmers offered milking cows supplements of cut-and-carry grass of other species, that is, of sugarcane and elephant grass, and that they would be willing to include a cut-and-carry shrub legume in this supplement.

These findings led to activities that originally had not been planned for, that is:

1. Contracting out to private seed companies of seed multiplication of new ecotypes of *Arachis* for the less fertile *mesones;* and

2. On-farm evaluation of the shrub legume *Codariocalyx gyroides*, which previous work had shown was well adapted to both the region and a cutting regime.

Experience from planting *Arachis* on several farms showed that proper and timely land preparation was important to ensure adequate

establishment by reducing weed competition. Lack of agricultural machinery was another obvious constraint to pasture establishment in the region. Thus, evaluating zero tillage methods for establishing *Arachis* in native and degraded pastures became important. Trials on zero tillage were established on farms to:

1. Compare how effectively different herbicides controlled vegetation;

2. Evaluate legume establishment in undisturbed soil and after applying herbicides; and

3. Evaluate legume establishment in disturbed soil and after applying herbicides.

In the original project proposal, economic studies on *Arachis* technology in the region were not included because emphasis was to be given to the legume's impact on animal production and soil enhancement. However, this exclusion was questioned by the Advisory Committee, who urged the project coordinator to carry out an *ex ante* economic analysis. The analysis determined:

1. Internal rates of return (IRR) associated with grass alone and with grass + *Arachis*, using biological parameters derived from previous research in the region and from the project; and

2. Sensitivity of IRR to changes in stocking rate, milk yield, and birth rates associated with *Arachis* technology and seed prices.

An additional study was later carried out to evaluate how participating and nonparticipating farmers accepted and adopted *Arachis*. It also better defined the constraints to adoption and incentives for increasing milk production.

From the start, we believed that the project's success would depend on ensuring that a major area of improved pastures was planted on 10 to 15 farms of the region. The strategy also considered that the 10 to 15 farmers initially selected to participate in the project would promote the *Arachis* technology to surrounding farmers. This, in turn, would ensure that a minimum of 100 farmers would be exposed and would likewise adopt the new pasture technology in the period covered by the project.

The above strategy did not work, given the prevalence of absentee owners participating directly in the project and the high cost of the *Arachis* seed available on the market. We had to develop an alternative diffusion approach for the extension phase of the project. The strategy that Nestlé promoted was to:

1. Create a technology transfer fund managed by Nestlé;

2. Conduct a survey among all milk producers who sell milk to Nestlé to define interest in recuperating degraded pastures using *Arachis*;

3. Contract the multiplication and purchase of commercial seed of *Arachis* to fulfill demand among interested producers;

4. Contract tractors for timely land preparation; and

5. Nestlé to give interest-free loans to farmers to partially off-set the cost of pasture establishment; the farmers would pay back with milk.

Involving beneficiaries

Once the project was launched, it turned out that most of the owners did not reside on their farms but managed them through periodic visits. Although owners, in most cases, made the final decisions on technical and nontechnical aspects that required financial investments, the day-to-day farm tasks were carried out by farm managers (or *mayordomos*), who usually had no formal education, received low pay, and had a high turnover. Consequently, the project's TAs had to constantly deal with new *mayordomos*.

The decisions in which farm owners participated consisted of:

1. Defining the location and size of pastures to reclaim;

2. Choosing and purchasing the grass species to associate with the legume;

3. Building fences to divide grazing areas;

4. Replanting newly established pastures;

5. Defining when and how to control weeds in the pastures;

6. Determining when to first graze newly established pastures; and

7. Determining grazing management (intensity and days on/days off) of well-established grass and grass/legume pastures.

Major Outcomes

The successes and failures of the 3-year-old project provide lessons for future pasture R&D projects in other tropical regions.

Successes

Undoubtedly the existence of a large and reliable market for fresh milk in the region influenced most of the participating and nonparticipating farmers to consider investing in reclaiming degraded pastures. The project's promotion of legumes also generated interest among livestock farmers in *Arachis* and its role in increasing milk yield and soil fertility.

The project helped find ways to facilitate and create incentives for adopting *Arachis*-based technology in the region. For example, it showed favorable *ex ante* economic results from *Arachis*, compared with the technology used by farmers. It also compared on-farm milk yields from pastures with *Arachis* with those from grass-alone pastures.

Ex ante economic data showed that the *Arachis* technology has a high IRR when compared with the traditional, grass-alone technology (Table 1), once the legume pasture increases daily milk production by 0.5 liters or more per cow.

Results from a farm where detailed measurements were carried out indicated that daily milk yield increased, on the average, from 0.2 to 0.5 liters per cow as a result of grazing the legume (Table 2). The results also indicated that the greatest milk yield response to the *Arachis*-based pasture was recorded in cows in the first and second stage of lactation and in Holstein crosses. Lascano and Avila (1993) had shown similar results in controlled experiments. Thus, to make the *Arachis* technology economically more attractive to farmers, the genetic potential of the milking herd must be improved through cross-breeding programs.

The *ex ante* economic analysis also showed that changes in calving rate

Table 1. Internal rates of return (IRR) associated with different pasture alternatives in dual-purpose cattle systems in the forest margins of Caquetá, Colombia.

Pasture	Pasture establishment cost (US$/ha)	Daily milk yield (L/cow)	Stocking rate (AU/ha)[a]	IRR (%)
Brachiaria decumbens	158	3.0	1.0	12.0
B. decumbens + Arachis pintoi	219	3.5	1.5	19.3
B. humidicola + A. pintoi	337	3.5	2.0	21.8
B. dictyoneura + A. pintoi	368	3.5	2.0	21.1

a. AU = animal unit (one cow and calf).

Table 2. Daily milk yield of cows grazing *Brachiaria* spp. with and without *Arachis pintoi* on a farm of the Nestlé Project, Department of Caquetá, Colombia.

Milk source	No. of observations	Milk yield from grazing (kg/cow)[a]	
		Brachiaria spp.	*Brachiaria* spp. + *A. pintoi*
Cows			
Holstein crosses	403	6.4 b	6.9 a
Other crosses	320	4.5 b	4.7 a
Stage of lactation			
1/3	250	6.1 b	6.6 a
2/3	220	5.9 b	6.2 a
3/3	253	4.9	5.1

a. Values in the same row with different letters are significantly different ($P < 0.05$).

Table 3. Sensitivity of internal rates of return caused by changes in production parameters associated with the *Arachis* technology[a].

Change (%)	Stocking rate (AU/ha)[b]	Daily milk yield (L/cow)	Calving rate (%)
0	19.3 (1.50)	19.3 (3.50)	19.3 (60)
+ 10	20.6 (1.65)	21.0 (3.86)	22.5 (66)
+ 20	21.6 (1.80)	22.7 (4.20)	25.8 (72)
+ 30	22.9 (1.95)	24.4 (4.55)	29.1 (78)
+ 40	23.9 (2.10)	26.1 (4.90)	32.6 (84)
+ 50	24.8 (2.25)	27.8 (5.25)	36.1 (90)

a. Values in parentheses correspond to the absolute value of each production parameter.
b. AU = animal unit (one cow and calf).

caused by *Arachis* would have the greatest effect on the IRR, compared with increases in stocking rate or daily milk yield (Table 3). Unfortunately, with the methodology used in the project to evaluate pastures (Lascano et al. 1997), we could not obtain unbiased estimates of calving rates in grass and grass/legume pastures.

Other contributions of the project were:

1. New *Arachis* ecotypes for specific "niches";

2. Alternative methods for establishing grass/legume pastures;

3. Local TAs trained in forage agronomy, pasture management, and PR methods;

4. Identification of fertilization requirements and alternative establishment methods for *Arachis* through student research for undergraduate theses from a local university;

5. Promotion, through field days and technical bulletins, of techniques for proper pasture establishment and grazing management; and

6. Identification of constraints to the adoption of *Arachis* (i.e., high seed cost, high labor requirements, and lack of machinery).

A failure that was a success in disguise was the attempt to demonstrate appropriate technology use. At one farm, the *Arachis* stand was completely lost. In the periodic visits to the farm, the project's TAs noticed that the grass (*Brachiaria brizantha* cv. Marandu), sown in association with *Arachis*, was too tall, affecting the legume's normal spread. The farmer was advised that the pasture needed immediate grazing by many animals for a few days to reduce competition on the *Arachis*, and thus loss of the legume. The farmer's experience was, however, that the grass had to seed before animals could be introduced into the newly sown pasture. The *Arachis* was lost soon after. This negative experience demonstrated to other farmers the importance of proper grazing management in pastures sown with *Arachis*.

Failures

A major failure stemmed from the selection of farmers who participated in the first phase of the project. The fact that most farmers were absentee owners made using a true PR approach impossible. The TAs' day-to-day contacts were with farm managers, who usually had little authority and usually felt no commitment to the project's aims. Feedback was thus poor, defeating an important objective of PR.

Farm owners and/or farm managers frequently did not collaborate in collecting milk yield data because they believed that the extra work required was not worth the effort. Some farm managers also felt that, by monitoring milk yields, the owner was demonstrating a lack of trust in their honorability. The net effect was that reliable milk yield data—a major objective of the project—were impossible to obtain from some farms.

Some of the original farms included in the project were sold and the new owners decided not to continue with their participation. Some pastures were therefore neither monitored nor their milk yields recorded.

Other failures that became evident as the project progressed were related to technical issues:

1. The grass seed purchased by farm owners often germinated poorly, resulting in the need to replant many of the pastures.

2. On some farms, carrying out a proper cow rotation system across the grass and grass/legume pastures was impossible, resulting in limited time for the animals to adjust to the legume. Legume intake was thus low (Carulla et al. 1991) and led to biased estimates of milk yield.

3. Some grass/legume pastures received low grazing pressure, because the animals in the milking herd were few and/or internal fences were missing. The effect of the legume on milk yield was possibly underestimated because cows tended to prefer the grass.

Conclusions: Lessons Learned

Moving from the experiment station to a livestock farm is a real challenge for pasture or livestock researchers because they cannot always achieve the degree of control needed for obtaining unbiased responses to treatments. Nonetheless, on-farm research is rewarding in that it provides valuable feedback to researchers and contributes to validating and diffusing improved forage-based technologies.

The project just described identified ways of facilitating the adoption of a legume-based technology for recuperating degraded pastures in dual-purpose cattle farms located in forest margins. Successes and failures documented during the course of the project afforded some important lessons:

Research methods must be flexible

On-farm research on livestock production systems cannot be rigid in design or experimental method. Research protocols have to be adjusted to each farm, because farms vary considerably in animal numbers and types, paddock types and dimensions, and grazing management.

Select resident farmers, not absentee owners

The chances of success in pasture/ livestock research depend heavily on farmers' attitudes toward change and on their participation in the research and validation of new technologies. Criteria for selecting farmers must therefore be clearly defined and time must be spent on selecting farmers through interviews and farm visits. Where possible, absentee owners (whether of small, medium-sized, or large farms) should not be included in on-farm pasture/livestock research, because they do not provide the necessary feedback to the process of technology development, nor do they adequately promote successful technology.

Have diffusion strategies in place

On-farm participatory research helps refine new pasture technologies and provides feedback to researchers, but, in itself, does not accomplish the ultimate goal of diffusing successful technologies. Thus, a well-defined strategy for diffusing new technology should be part of the overall objective of a pasture/livestock R&D project. Such a strategy should include the elements of timely availability of inputs (i.e., seed, fertilizers, herbicides, and agriculture machinery) and credit.

Verify the existence of reliable markets for farm produce

Most farmers, regardless of farm size, appear willing to invest in improved pasture technologies as long as they have reliable markets for farm produce (i.e., steers, fresh milk, and cheese). Theoretically, the presence of a milk-processing industry will create a demand for more and better quality milk; farmers will thus be motivated to invest in improving pastures, herd potential, and farm infrastructure. A pasture development project should therefore be directed mainly at regions where markets for beef or milk exist or where a potential demand can be fulfilled.

Collect information on the likely demand and acceptability of a new technology

The acceptability and profitability of new pastures to farmers will be the ultimate determinants of adoption of improved pasture technologies. In this project, information on the legume's profitability and acceptability was gathered after fieldwork began. Thus, before a pasture/livestock project begins, "rapid rural appraisal" surveys should be conducted to obtain adequate baseline information on the likely demand for pasture technologies. Possible constraints for adopting technologies should also be identified through resource optimization simulation models. Finally, the potential profitability of a pasture technology being promoted should be investigated, using *ex ante* economic analyses. To help promote a new pasture technology, input and output data recorded on the farms should be used for detailed economic analysis at the project's end.

Find and involve committed institutions

An objective of the project was to train TAs of agricultural institutions in the region to make them aware of the technology being promoted and to provide the basis of participatory approaches for technology transfer. Unfortunately, the multiplier effect that was expected through training was not accomplished. An overriding reason for the failure was that the institutions represented by the trainees were not committed to transferring technology for pasture reclamation. Future projects should therefore identify relevant institutions in the region, and define their R&D plans, before committing resources to training their technical staff. A multiplier effect is thus more likely to be accomplished.

References

Carulla JE; Lascano CE; Ward JK. 1991. Selectivity of resident and esophageal-fistulated steers grazing *Arachis pintoi* and *Brachiaria dictyoneura* in the Llanos of Colombia. Trop Grassl 25:317-324.

Grof B. 1985. Forage attributes of the perennial groundnut *Arachis pintoi* in a tropical savanna environment in Colombia. In: Proc. XV International Grassland Congress, Kyoto, Japan. Science Council of Japan and Japanese Society of Grassland Science, Nishi-nasuno, Tochigi-ken, Japan. p 168-170.

Lascano C. 1994. Nutritive value and animal production of forage *Arachis*. In: Kerridge PC; Hardy B, eds. Biology and agronomy of forage *Arachis*. CIAT, Cali, Colombia. p 109-121.

Lascano C; Avila P. 1991. Potencial de producción de leche en pasturas solas y asociadas con leguminosas adaptadas a suelos ácidos. Pasturas Trop 13:2-10.

Lascano C; Avila P. 1993. Milk yield of cows with different genetic potential on grass and grass-legume tropical pastures. In: XVII International Grassland Congress. Proc. 18-21 Feb. 1993, Rockhampton, Australia. New Zealand Grassland Association and others, Palmerston North, New Zealand. Vol. 3, session 55, p 2006-2007.

Lascano C; Estrada J. 1989. Long-term productivity of legume-based and pure grass pastures in the Eastern Plains of Colombia. In: Proc. XVI International Grassland Congress, Nice, France. p 1177-1178.

Lascano C; Thomas RJ. 1988. Forage quality and animal selection of *Arachis pintoi* in association with tropical grasses in the Eastern Plains of Colombia. Grass Forage Sci 43:433-439.

Lascano C; Avila P; Ramírez G. 1997. Aspectos metodológicos en la evaluación de pasturas en fincas con ganado de doble propósito. Pasturas Trop 18:65-70.

Michelsen H. 1990. Análisis del desarrollo de la producción de leche en la zona tropical húmeda: El caso de Caquetá, Colombia. Working document no. 60. Tropical Forages Program, CIAT, Cali, Colombia. 68 p.

Ramírez A; Seré C. 1990. *Brachiaria decumbens* en Caquetá: Adopción y uso en ganadería de doble propósito. Working document no. 67. Tropical Forages Program, CIAT, Cali, Colombia. 68 p.

Rincón A; Cuesta P; Pérez R; Lascano C; Ferguson J. 1992. Maní forrajero perenne (*Arachis pintoi* Krapovickas and Gregory). Boletín técnico no. 219. Instituto Colombiano Agropecuario (ICA), Bogotá, Colombia. 18 p.

Toledo JM. 1985. Pasture development for cattle production in the major ecosystems of the American lowlands. In: Proc. XV International Grassland Congress, Kyoto, Japan. Science Council of Japan and Japanese Society of Grassland Science, Nishi-nasuno, Tochigi-ken, Japan. p 74-78.

Toledo JM; Nores G. 1986. Tropical pastures technology for marginal lands of tropical America. Outlook Agric 15:3-9.

Tothill JC; Hargreaves JNG; Jones RM. 1978. BOTANAL: a comprehensive sampling and computing procedure for estimating pasture yield and composition, 1: Field sampling. Tropical Agronomy Technical Memorandum no. 8. Division of Tropical Crops and Pastures, Commonwealth Scientific and Industrial Research Organisation (CSIRO), Brisbane, Queensland, Australia. 20 p.

Ulrich C; Vera R; Weniger JH. 1994. Producción de leche con vacas de doble propósito en pasturas solas y asociadas con leguminosas. Pasturas Trop 16:27-30.

CHAPTER 6

Adapting Participatory Research Methods for Developing Integrated Crop Management for Cassava-Based Systems, Northeast Brazil

B. Ospina, L. Smith, and *A. C. Bellotti**

Project Objectives and Institutional Relationships

A two-pronged project was carried out to help alleviate poverty and increase food security by increasing the ecologically sustainable productivity of small-scale, cassava-based, agricultural systems in Africa and Latin America. Funded by the United Nations Development Programme (UNDP) during 1993-1997, the project had the specific goal of developing "Ecologically Sustainable Cassava Plant Protection in South America and Africa: An Environmentally Sound Approach" ("Proteção Fitossanitária Sustentável de Mandioca" or "PROFISMA" in Brazil). It involved activities in both West Africa and Northeast Brazil, using farmer participatory research (FPR) methods to develop, test, and adopt integrated pest management (IPM), integrated crop management, and biological control.

This paper focuses on the FPR activities in Brazil. The project had two main objectives. First, it worked to develop networks of trained farmers, extension workers, and researchers

familiar with the elements of sustainable crop production and IPM. Second, it tested and adapted ecologically sound, technology components with farmers, who provided feedback on options for facilitating the adoption of improved technology. Developing and adopting effective technologies for crop protection were meant to help reduce crop losses from pest attacks and prevent pesticide use, thus stabilizing cassava yield and root quality. These technologies would also help maintain agricultural sustainability in tropical, rainfed areas of low soil fertility. Farmers, extension workers, and researchers were trained for this project and to help its continuance.

Problems Addressed and Beneficiaries

Problems that arose

Brazil is the second largest producer of cassava in the world (25.5 million tons; FAO 1995), about half of which is grown in the Northeast. The population of this extremely poor region is considered by the Food and Agriculture Organization of the United Nations (FAO) to have a major deficiency of dietary calories. Cassava is important in this region because the

* CIAT, Cali, Colombia.

environmental conditions (poor soil fertility and low rainfall) are unfavorable for the cultivation of most other crops. The region typically has only a minimal infrastructure of roads, electricity, and services. Most cassava farmers cultivate plots of less than 2 ha, with an average yield of 10.8 t/ha, compared with the average for the rest of Brazil at about 17.1 t/ha and the crop's potential of about 30 t/ha. The states of Bahia, Ceará, Pernambuco, and Paraíba were targeted by this project because of their importance as cassava-producing regions, and the widespread incidence of pests. The existence of complementary activities in the area, being carried out by CIAT and the Empresa Brasileira de Pesquisa Agropecuária (EMBRAPA), also influenced selection.

The project's aim was to increase food security and reduce environmental degradation by developing and transferring new technologies for pest control to small-scale cassava farmers. Previous transfer of technology from research centers such as the Centro Nacional de Pesquisa de Mandioca e Fruticultura Tropical (CNPMF) and CIAT had been slow. To address this problem, an FPR philosophy was included in the project. This, in turn, meant training farmers, state extension workers, and national program scientists in FPR methods and the execution of on-farm participatory experiments.

Problem diagnosis

CIAT and Brazilian scientists familiar with small-scale, cassava production systems in Northeast Brazil developed the project proposal. They identified what they thought were the principal constraints to cassava production in the region: cassava green mite (*Mononychellus tanajoa*) (CGM), cassava mealybug (*Phenacoccus herreni*), root rots (*Phytophthora* spp.,

Fusarium spp., *Pythium* spp.), and cassava vein mosaic virus (CVMV).

Starting in 1993, the project first conducted an extensive survey to assess farmer opinions regarding constraints to increased productivity. The survey included 1672 farmers in 74 communities in four states (Table 1). A limitation was that farmers naturally emphasized problems of high visibility (e.g., galls or hornworms), regardless of their actual impact and overlooked less visible ones (e.g., viruses or mites). Nonetheless, this provided a starting point for prioritizing research areas and for better communication between farmers and scientists.

In 18 communities, groups of farmers were locally elected to conduct FPR experiments. A subsequent intensive survey of farmer opinions of these groups, known as Committees for Local Agricultural Research (CLARs), helped obtain more precise (although still subjective) estimates of the relative importance of principal cassava pests (Figure 1). Mites and leafcutting ants joined root rots and hornworms as being top priority pests.

Collaborators and beneficiaries

The project involved direct collaboration between CIAT and the following:

1. Four EMBRAPA agricultural research centers: CNPMF, the Centro Nacional de Pesquisa de Monitoramento e Avaliação de Impacto Ambiental (CNPMA), Centro de Pesquisa Agropecuária de Clima Temperado (CPACT), and Centro de Pesquisa Agropecuária do Trópico Semi-Árido (CPATSA);

2. Five Brazilian state research agencies: Empresa Bahiana de Agricultura (EBDA), Empresa Pernambucana de Pesquisa

Table 1. The top five constraints to cassava productivity in Northeast Brazil according to farmer opinions documented in the PROFISMA[a] extensive survey, 1993.

Constraint	Priority ranking[b]				Overall priority[c]
	Bahia	Ceará	Pernambuco	Paraíba	
Lack of credit	1	1	1	2	11.0
Root rots	-	-	3	1	8.3
Poor soil	3	-	2	3	6.2
Low cassava prices	-	2	3	4	5.0
Lack of land	-	4	5	-	3.5
Hornworm	2	5	-	-	2.9
Drought	4	3	-	-	2.8
Commercialization	-	-	-	5	1.4
Leaf galls	5	-	-	-	1.2
Stemborers	-	-	-	5	0.7
Number surveyed					Total
Communities	25	20	19	10	74
Farmers	472	549	377	274	1672

a   PROFISMA = Proteção Fitossanitária Sustentável de Mandioca, Brazil.
b. Rank 1 = first priority, based on total of all communities surveyed within a given state.
c. Number of priority points (rank 1 = 5 points; rank 5 = 1 point) summed over all communities, but the value for each state was adjusted by the number of communities in the state before totaling.

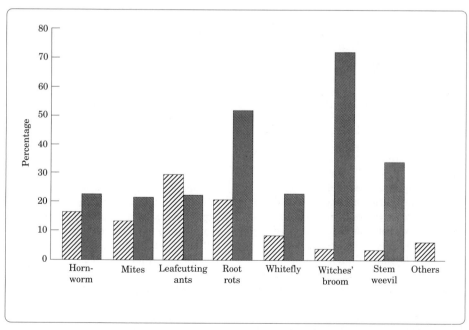

Figure 1. Importance of cassava pests in Northeast Brazil according to growers in an intensive survey of farmers in 18 communities where Committees for Local Agricultural Research (CLARs) were established. (▨ = infection; ■ = yield loss.)

Agropecuária (IPA), Empresa Estadual de Pesquisa Agropecuária da Paraíba, S.A. (EMEPA), Empresa de Pesquisa Agropecuária do Ceará (EPACE), and Empresa de Desenvolvimento Agropecuária de Sergipe (EMDAGRO);

3. Four Brazilian state extension agencies: Empresa de Pesquisa, Assistência Técnica e Extensão Rural do Ceará (EMATER-CE); Empresa de Pesquisa, Assistência Técnica e Extensão Rural do Paraíba (EMATER-PB); Empresa de Pesquisa, Assistência Técnica e Extensão Rural do Pernambuco (EMATER-PE); and the extension service of EBDA; and

4. Four Brazilian universities: Universidade Federal de Alagoas (UFAL), Universidade Estadual do Ceará (UEC), Universidade Estadual de Campinas (UNICAMP), and Universidade Federal da Bahia (UFBA).

CIAT also interacted with the International Institute of Tropical Agriculture (IITA), Benin, Africa, and some advanced research institutions in developed countries. CIAT and CNPMF shared the coordination of project activities in Northeast Brazil.

Farmers were direct beneficiaries (about 300 in 25 CLARs), as were the Brazilian extension (30) and research personnel (12) with whom we worked. Indirect beneficiaries included other farmers in the region who attended farmer field days and were exposed to the new technologies being adopted, women who processed the cassava roots into *farinha* (flour), and farmer families who benefited from increased food and income.

The expected impact of the project was to increase cassava yield, decrease soil deterioration, help increase rural prosperity, and increase the capability of national agricultural research systems (NARS) scientists and extension officers to solve production problems.

Research Methods Used

Research methods were based on the FPR methods described by Ashby (1990) and Stroud (1993). We adopted this methodology for two reasons. First, we sought to develop institutional human resources in the area of FPR methods. Second, a goal was to establish technology testing activities on IPM at the community level to facilitate involving farmers in technology design, development, and transfer. Both the training and the FPR strategy were aimed at developing an analytical framework for priority setting and planning. On-farm activities included diagnosis, establishing CLARs, planning, experimentation, and evaluation.

Information collected in the extensive survey (Table 1) was used to identify 18 communities that represented a range of different, high-priority problems. After a short training period and the election of four farmers per community, CLARs were established in each of these communities. Each CLAR was provided with US$400 as seed money to finance the first cycle of technology testing, with the intention that this would become a revolving fund. Some problems to investigate were selected in each CLAR; and on-farm experiments were planned, set up, and maintained for a full crop cycle (18 months). At harvest, the farmers and FPR trainers evaluated the plants and yield for each treatment, using both quantitative and subjective observations.

For example, farmers in Aporá, Bahia, chose root rots, CGM, inappropriate use of fertilizers, and lack of a local artisanal flour mill (*casa de farinha*) as their top four constraints to increasing productivity. These farmers comprised a poor community where cassava yield was less than one-third that of a nearby community. The farmers established a CLAR, naming it "Chapada", and chose to test technologies that would help control root rots. An experiment was planned and executed to test two cassava varieties—a preferred local variety, Cemitério, and a resistant variety, Osso Duro, recommended by scientists at CNPMF. The experiment also tested two planting methods—on ridges as recommended by CNPMF or on flat land as commonly done by farmers, using four replicates in a randomized complete block design (32 plants per block).

The average root yield of the CNPMF variety (10.1 t/ha) was lower than that of the local one (15.9 t/ha) (Figure 2), indicating a failure of the resistant variety (which was also observed at other CLAR trials). This has led to 'Cemitério' being eliminated from CNPMF's root-rot-resistance breeding program. Planting cassava stakes on ridges increased the yield of both 'Osso Duro' (26%) and 'Cemitério' (45%), compared with planting on flat land. The farmers' subjective rankings of overall performance indicated a high preference for the local variety, but with ridge planting.

Both farmers and scientists benefited from this first experimental contact. The CLAR initiated a subsequent experiment to evaluate more varieties from CNPMF. We realized after the evaluation of the first experiment that the farmers' observations and opinions on the advantages and disadvantages of the different varieties had been insufficiently recorded. This fault was corrected in the second experiment to provide more feedback to the plant breeders.

Method selection

Selection of research methods was based on available information and experiences at CIAT and EMBRAPA-CNPMF with cassava research and development in the region. The FPR strategy and training methods were based on previous experiences with the Investigación Participativa en Agricultura (IPRA) project in Colombia (Ashby 1990). At each CLAR, the farmers and researchers discussed the problems to be studied and selected the technologies to be tested.

Project development

The diagnostic survey of farmer opinions confirmed the perceived importance of some of the pest constraints such as CGM, cassava mealybug, and root rots. However, it identified others that originally had not been considered: witches' broom, leafcutting ants, poor soil quality, and lack of credit (to buy fertilizer). Although some of these, such as changing governmental credit policies, were clearly outside the scope of the project, we were still able to respond to this information. We did so by shifting project resources to increase support of research on plant pathology and agronomy. It became clear in the final stages that the sustained impact of the project would depend on increasing and stabilizing the value of cassava. This may be best done by developing markets for processed cassava products that have an elastic demand, such as dried chips for animal feed, or starch for industrial uses. These components have been incorporated into proposals to fund future activities.

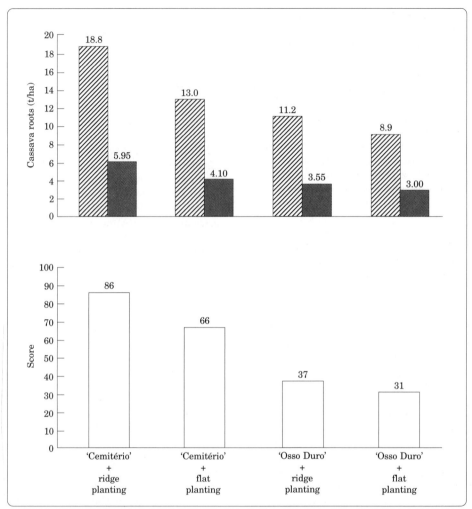

Figure 2. Evaluation of a local cassava variety ('Cemitério') with a recommended variety ('Osso Duro') for resistance and planting practices to control root rots. Trials were conducted by the Chapada Committee for Local Agricultural Research (CLAR), Aporá, Bahia, Brazil. (▨ = cassava root yield; ■ = dry matter content; □ = farmer's preference ranking evaluation.)

Problems encountered

Initially, most CNPMF scientists were skeptical and did not collaborate with the first on-farm trials. They considered the PROFISMA project as requiring an increase in their workload without financial compensation. They distrusted the outside leaders (CIAT),

and knew little about FPR. By the second year, however, several CNPMF scientists, who were not directly funded by PROFISMA, began participating in on-farm trials, particularly in root rots, crop rotation, and cover-crop companion plants. By the third year, all the CNPMF scientists working with cassava were involved, to varying degrees, with on-farm trials. In contrast, the state extension agents adopted the FPR strategy quickly, and collaborated eagerly. This difference of attitude is partly a result of the project providing extension agents with badly needed funding for transport to field sites and of helping to elevate their professional status.

The usual problems of personality and cultural conflicts arose, and the split leadership between CIAT and CNPMF caused administrative problems. Leadership also suffered discontinuity in that the CNPMF Director and Research Director were replaced partway through the project. However, this proved beneficial because the new directors both favored the FPR philosophy and fostered further collaboration with CIAT. The CIAT leader of PROFISMA left after the third year, undermining our ability to obtain funding for a second phase.

The project has been much more influential at the individual level than at the institutional level within the states. Both CNPMF and EMBRAPA have embraced this project as an example of how they want to do most of their research in the future. However, the state extension agencies have not responded to the needs of their agents who participated, nor have they begun to show a shift toward client-oriented prioritization of their activities. The state agencies have also been unable to maintain funding levels of extension activities as the project phased out. Part of this failure might have been avoided had we trained and interacted more with administrators, and had we scheduled financing of the phase out well in advance. Even so, the failure of the donor to extend project funding for a second phase was a surprise to us all.

Another important constraint has been the lack of support from the research agencies that were involved in the project, including EMBRAPA. Few researchers across the region had been willing to participate in training activities and to later act as advisors in planning and evaluating technology testing trials. This has placed an added burden on the work of the extension service.

Implementing participatory research

Beneficiaries were involved from the start of the project when the local extension service for the Extensive Diagnoses selected the farmer communities. Later, in 19 selected communities, farmer groups accepted the proposal to form CLARs. These became the coordinating bodies for planning and decision making related to the technology trials to be executed in their community. Activities for CLARs included determining objectives, designing strategies, installing and administering the trials, evaluating experiment results, and considering alternative solutions. These were all done in collaboration with national program scientists and state extension workers, but farmers played a leading role. The CLARs also participated in other complementary activities such as exchange visits with other CLARs and visits to EMBRAPA's cassava research station. In some cases, CLARs independently initiated additional research activities with other crops grown in their communities. Some CLARs further contributed to the implementing agencies because they served as sites for training events and for demonstrating the project's impact to visiting scientists, administrators, and donors, helping to educate those who make decisions that can affect more people. Such visits are helping to spread the FPR technique to other crops such as onions, sweet pepper, and passion fruit.

Results in Terms of Problem Solving

Successes in technical problem solving

Some areas of PROFISMA research, such as biological control of CGM and cassava mealybug, proceeded with little FPR involvement. However, when EMBRAPA scientists used hand lenses to show the farmers that damaged plants had mites, the farmers quickly learned how to observe and record levels of infestation. Once having learned that the scientists were conducting research on predatory mites, the farmers immediately wanted to know how they could get these to control CGM. Scientists were surprised and became alert to the possibility of using augmentative releases or of developing cultural control practices with the farmers to help conserve natural enemy populations—strategies they had previously thought impractical.

Although available results remain limited because of the project's short period of execution (the second season of participatory experiments is being harvested this year), some important results can be mentioned. The first is the impact of improved varieties in traditional farming systems, especially when these varieties have previously passed through participatory selection processes (Table 2). In most cases, the varieties recommended by CNPMF scientists outyielded local ones, thus rapidly increasing productivity. Trials involving FPR should also increase the frequency with which improved varieties are successfully introduced into farming systems. Second, the use of improved management practices (selection of planting material, that is, of stem cuttings; planting density; planting on ridges; and intercropping)

indicated good potential for increasing productivity and sustainability of cassava cultivation systems in the region. Biological control of the cassava mealybug (*Phenacoccus herreni*) was also extremely successful, although this did not involve FPR.

The CNPMF used information from the extensive and intensive diagnostic surveys and the FPR CLAR experiences to help set their research priorities. New project proposals that CNPMF staff wrote were based on the PROFISMA project's favorable results and on their revised priorities. These include crop and soil management, training of FPR trainers, disseminating and FPR-evaluating improved varieties, IPM, and postharvest processing. A development project in the State of Sergipe, the "Projeto de Apoio as Familias de Baixa Renda da Região Semi-Árida" (PROSERTAO), financed by the International Fund for Agricultural Development (IFAD), specifically requested PROFISMA collaborators from CNPMF to propose FPR activities to be financed by PROSERTAO. EMBRAPA has also praised the success of the PROFISMA project and has adopted FPR as a guiding philosophy for doing research, which suggests a big impact on Brazilian government policy. The CNPMF is now promoting the use of FPR in their other mandated crops.

Failures in technical problem solving

Some targeted problems were not solved during the project's 4 years, although substantial progress was made. That technical solutions have not yet been developed for some of the problems is not surprising. Biological control of CGM by introducing exotic predatory mites has not yet been achieved, even though systems to introduce, multiply, and release more

Table 2. Summary of the principal results of the first season of farmer participatory research (FPR) trials involving Committees for Local Agricultural Research (CLARs), Bahia, Brazil.

CLAR	Problem	Technology tested	Yield increase (%)	Dry matter increase (%)	Notes
Colônia Agrícola "Roberto Santos"	Low yield	Varieties	0 to +27	+4 to +33	Evaluation of regional varieties only; two yielded >35 t/ha (extremely high). The local variety (check) yielded lowest, but had second highest preference.
Colônia Agrícola "Roberto Santos"	Cassava green mite	Resistance	na[a]	na[a]	Farmers were trained to make quantitative measurements of mite damage levels.
Chapada	Root rots	Resistance	-32 to -40	-27 to -40	CNPMF[b] variety failed to show good resistance and was discarded from its breeding program.
Chapada	Root rots	Cultivation	+26 to +45	+18 to +45	Planting on ridges, a new method, was most successful and preferred by farmers.
Buril	Cassava green mite	Resistance	-15 to +32	-28 to +34	Two of four new varieties yielded higher than local ones, but the farmers still tended to prefer the best local variety. Farmers were trained to make quantitative measurements of mite damage levels.
Cadete	Soil fertility	Fertilizer	-6 to -10	-1 to -3	Chemical fertilizers were expensive and did not increase yield.
Cadete	Soil fertility	Compost	-15 to +64	-11 to +67	Farmers preferred highest yield technology. Interaction between two local varieties and yield response.
Barra	Whitefly	Resistance	+6 to +51	-17 to +55	Three new varieties yielded higher than local ones. Farmers preferred new variety with highest yield.
Umbuzeiro	Soil fertility	Legume companion	-65 to -74	-66 to -75	Poor experiment because of lack of supervision by researchers, and premature technology.
Umbuzeiro	Soil fertility	Row spacing	+5	+10	Farmers did not prefer higher yielding new technology.

a. na = not applicable.
b. CNPMF = Centro Nacional de Pesquisa de Mandioca e Fruticultura Tropical, Brazil.

than 120,000 predators have been developed. One type does show signs of establishment. Although CIAT has identified cassava varieties that are ready to be transferred to EMBRAPA for breeding and evaluation, varietal resistance to whiteflies remains to be accomplished. Laboratory methods for isolating and identifying root-rot pathogens and for testing the susceptibility of cassava varieties have been developed and are ready for transfer to Brazilian scientists, but much work needs to be done to develop resistant varieties or commercially viable biological control. Polymerase chain reaction (PCR) methods to detect plant material infested with CVMV have been developed, making feasible the conducting of trials to measure impact and evaluate resistance. Intercropping with legumes has not yet shown benefits with respect to increasing cassava yields. On-farm trials, testing leguminous cover crops, were outright failures, primarily because the scientists had tested neither plants nor management methods well.

Lessons learned

Some of the cassava varieties that were recommended by CNPMF for resistance to or tolerance of root rots seem to have lost their potential or to have only limited levels of resistance. Some farmer varieties, previously unknown to the Center's plant breeders, performed better than the improved varieties, representing new sources of germplasm for breeding. Some farmer groups are already obtaining yields that are higher (>30 t/ha) than the national and local averages, confirming that farmers in this region can realistically achieve substantial improvements in yield (50%-200%).

Involving beneficiaries in participatory research

The farmer beneficiaries were involved at several levels in this project. First, their inputs during the initial diagnostic surveys were used to set priorities for strategic research. Second, the CLARs determined the problems on which they wanted to work in their on-farm participatory trials and which of the available technologies they wanted to test. Third, the farmers participated with scientists to evaluate the results of their trials and decide what other solutions could be developed in the cases where the tested technologies were inadequate.

The members participated with suggestions, ideas, and their own experiences in the design of the trials conducted in each community. Throughout the process, farmers assumed responsibility for trial management. They also evaluated the trials, which included an agronomic appraisal of the experiment (yield, root dry matter, and mass of aerial parts) and an evaluation according to farmers' opinions and perceptions of the results. In each case, farmers ranked the different treatments, selected their own best treatments, and compared their findings with those of the agronomic evaluation. These results were used as a basis for a second experiment. The very fact that most CLARs planted a second experiment (some are already planning the third) indicates farmers' interest in the methodology and their willingness to assume specific roles and share responsibilities with local agencies in developing and testing new technologies.

Additional benefits from the use of this participatory method are that farmers' groups have improved their own organization. They are able to define and prioritize their problems, communicate them to research and extension agencies, and mobilize local leadership to collaborate as efficient, reliable partners with the institutions.

Various failures occurred with the use of the participatory method. These included:

1. Farmer groups were poorly selected in some cases.

2. Additional training and follow-up activities of trainees were lacking, related to the use of more complete evaluation methods (identification and recording of farmers' criteria).

3. More training activities with farmer groups were needed, specifically oriented toward developing skills and internal organization to make groups more efficient at pressuring research and extension systems so that their needs and constraints are taken into account.

Reasons for Successes and Failures

Successes

Team leaders experienced in FPR approaches and methodologies that had already been tested helped the relatively rapid success of the training and the execution of FPR field experiments. Brazilian researchers, extension workers, and farmers more easily adopted and assimilated the FPR method because of a well-designed portfolio of training materials and manuals on the CLAR methodology previously developed by the IPRA project. Also contributing to success, was the design of the training activities, which fitted directly into project activities, allowing trainees access to experiment sites where they

could practice and gain experience with the skills and methods being taught.

The training's success was reflected by the farmers quickly responding and showing interest in organizing CLARs in their communities and taking up new roles and responsibilities in technology-testing activities. Their commitment to the FPR activities became a powerful tool to ensure that their needs and priorities, and their opinions and criteria about ranking alternative solutions, would start to be included in setting research agendas at EMBRAPA and CIAT. Finally, local research and extension agencies already had available many technologies with the potential to solve some of the problems the farmers identified. They simply needed to be delivered to and tested with farmer groups to promote their adoption.

Failures and problems

Several factors limited the potential success of our project. Extension workers had lower salaries and fewer operating funds than national program researchers. This reduced their interest and motivation to participate in new farmer-responsive research and extension activities. Further, the project did not provide collaborating state extension agencies with enough financial resources to implement FPR activities. In most cases, these agencies ended up allocating their own resources to finance project activities at the local level. Consequently, the strengthening, internalizing, and expanding of the use of FPR-based methods within these institutions became entirely dependent on their own internal planning and priority setting processes. Unfortunately, the research and extension agencies collaborating with the project are currently being forced to reduce costs and downsize, thus jeopardizing their FPR activities.

The inherent project goal to create mechanisms to enhance the bottom-up flow of information from farmers has been difficult to achieve. Local agencies lacked systems for collecting this information. Also, the short execution period of project activities has not allowed us to consolidate, analyze, and publish the information resulting from the technology trials in a form that can be used to influence research planning and decision-making processes.

A final factor is that the farmer groups lack political power, sufficient organizational skills, and funds to have significant influence on political decision makers. This is particularly important because lack of credit to help farmers buy fertilizer or adopt new technologies depends more on the general government than the research or extension agencies. In some communities, the CLAR's establishment was the first collective action toward the overall goal of improving their situation. Developing the skills and abilities of farmer groups will demand a long-term approach, and specific initiatives will need to be developed to respond to this weakness.

In our opinion, none of the above factors are specific to the culture or history of Northeast Brazil. Our experience with similar projects in several other countries suggests that these factors are usually present in other Latin American countries.

Major Lessons Learned

Lessons learned

The following lessons were learned from the study:

1. Human resource development strategies to stimulate dissemination of the use of FPR-based methods among local research and extension agencies are effective, cost efficient, and have impact.

2. Current strategies used by local agencies for identifying problems, setting priorities, and evaluating alternative technological solutions lack a systematic approach to incorporate farmers' needs and priorities in their decision-making process to define research agendas and portfolios. Using FPR-based methods helped bridge this gap.

3. Local research and extension agencies do not have systematic, reliable methods to predict and assess adoption rates of the technologies being delivered. Consequently, we have been unable to estimate how efficient or cost effective FPR has been, overall, on the technology generation and transfer process.

4. Farmer groups are able to assimilate the CLAR methodology for generating and transferring improved, integrated, crop management technologies. The new roles, knowledge, responsibilities, and information are compatible with their current literacy levels. The committees of experimenting farmers formed by the communities have been able to assimilate the principles of controlled comparison, replication, and random assignment of treatments. They have been able to apply these to the design, setting up, administration, and evaluation of their own technology testing trials.

5. Alternative technology solutions previously untested at the farm

level should not be proposed to inexperienced CLARs because of the high risk of failure. The risk of losing farmers' confidence and enthusiasm is too high. Instead, it is better to build their confidence in the first experiment with simple technologies that are most likely to provide positive results. In our project, initial results with crop rotation, intercropping, or mulching practices, to which farmers reacted negatively, made it more difficult to encourage them to continue testing other technologies.

6. Technology components currently available to local research and extension agencies, especially improved crop varieties, could have a significant role in improving yields, productivity, and stability of cassava-based systems in most of the regions where the project has been conducting activities.

How the method can be improved

Our experience with the project suggests that changes could be made to improve the method used. We suggest the following:

1. Slightly change the training model to reinforce the module on participatory evaluation methods that should be taught to trainees when the field experiments are ready for harvest. This will enable them to practice, with the farmers, the use of the methods. Also, incorporate a more intensive follow-up mechanism, with trainers supervising and helping trainees when they use the methods in real contexts.

2. Introduce strategies to more systematically manage the information generated by the CLARs and their technology

adaptation work. Annual or semiannual planning and review meetings should be designed and budgeted to create opportunities for periodic analysis of results.

3. Introduce additional strategies to collect, synthesize, and package information from CLAR activities so that recommendations can be delivered to decision makers and eventually incorporated into the research planning and decision-making processes.

4. Dedicate more effort to strengthening the administrative, managerial, and organizational skills of farmer groups, improving their capabilities for communication and negotiation with national research and extension systems.

5. Allocate more "seed" economic resources for institutions that are initiating activities with FPR-based research and extension activities. This would help overcome the initial resistance to change and neutralize the perceived risks of trying out a new method of doing research and development. The cost-benefit impact of this approach could be large because once these agencies are able to assess the impact of these client-oriented methods on technology generation, transfer, and adoption, they will incorporate them into their organizational structures.

Assessing the costs and benefits of using a participatory approach

Quantitatively based analysis is not an easy task. Although the technical results can be measured thus (root yield or dry matter content), the real benefits of FPR are increased adoption rate of improved technologies and feedback to scientists to help them develop appropriate technologies to solve the most critical problems. This analysis would require longer time horizons and a "control" (e.g., scientists-extension workers-farmers using FPR versus those not using it), which is practically impossible to obtain. The best remaining option is to do a before-and-after analysis of adoption rates. In our case, perhaps the most obvious measure is the rapid adoption of "old" technologies that were not known to the farmers before our project began. In most of the first season trials, root yield increased by 25%-50% and dry matter content by 20%-55%. Dissemination of these cassava varieties and crop management practices throughout the region would have enormous economic impact.

The amount of information generated from CLAR FPR experiments within a short period of time is impressive. Scientists are now learning what the real production problems are in various regions. Likewise, they are learning what technological solutions are truly practical. New germplasm has become available to plant breeders. More new technologies are being offered directly to farmer communities. CLARs have also helped the research community by effectively providing a local service to field-test technologies at a minimal cost.

The CLARs are beginning their third consecutive season of experiments, which indicates that the participating farmers feel the results are certainly worthwhile. Yet quantitative data are lacking to evaluate the benefits. We need adoption and impact studies that interview farmers and make a before-and-after comparative analysis, but lack of continued project funding prevents this.

Another strong indicator of impact is the recent portfolio of five new project proposals developed by CNPMF and recently presented to EMBRAPA. The objectives of these proposals were based on the FPR results of our project, and they all involve the use of participatory research methods for technology development and transfer. One proposal explicitly focuses on the Brazilian research staff implementing and internalizing FPR methods. EMBRAPA was so impressed by the results of our 4-year project that they have adopted it as a model of how they want to do research in the future.

Conclusions

After 4 years, Brazilian scientists, extension workers, and national administrators have perceived this project as having been extremely successful. Scientists, externally commissioned to review its technical achievements, have also praised our results. Initial resistance by many national program scientists to the idea of working directly with farmers has dissipated, and many have become enthusiastic supporters of FPR. Using end-users to help prioritize problems and to identify and evaluate technological solutions is revolutionizing the way of doing research at CNPMF, and is being adopted by EMBRAPA as a central philosophy.

International donors are also recognizing this impact, as indicated by IFAD's insistence that its new development project in Sergipe benefit from collaboration with CNPMF scientists. Nonetheless, this project has encountered many problems, and because of the long, 18-month crop cycle of cassava in Northeast Brazil, only two cycles of field experiments have been conducted. This is too short a time to obtain institutionalization of this method or to obtain quantitative analysis of its impact on farmer welfare and the productivity of Brazilian scientists and extension workers. Unfortunately, we have been unable to obtain funding of a second phase, so many of our gains risk being lost. Nonetheless, both CIAT and CNPMF have submitted proposals to other donors in the hope of continuing this work to ensure that the changes become more permanent.

References

Ashby J. 1990. Evaluating technology with farmers: a handbook. Investigación Participativa en Agricultura/ *Participatory Research in Agriculture* (IPRA), CIAT, Cali, Colombia. 95 p.

FAO (Food and Agriculture Organization of the United Nations). 1995. Databases. <http://www.fao.org/WAICENT/Agricul.htm>

Stroud A. 1993. Conducting on-farm experiments. CIAT, Cali, Colombia. 118 p.

CHAPTER 7

Soil Conservation Strategies That Take into Account Farmer Perspectives

K. Müller-Sämann*, F. Flörchinger**, L. E. Girón***,
J. Restrepo**, and D. Leihner**

Introduction

CIAT and Hohenheim University are collaborating in a project on "Soil Degradation and Crop Productivity Research for Conservation Technology Development in Andean Hillside Farming". The project is funded by the Bundesministerium für Wirtschaftliche Zusammenarbeit und Entwicklung (BMZ; or the "Federal Ministry for Economic Cooperation and Development" in English). Begun in 1993, the project builds on previous work in this area by the CIAT Cassava Program and on a project investigating basic aspects of soil erosion and the factors and processes governing erosion on Andean Inceptisols (Reining 1992; Ruppenthal 1995; Ruppenthal et al. 1996).

Cassava forage legume intercropping and its potential for sustainable cassava production on acid, low fertility hillsides of the tropical mid-altitudes were also examined. The new project additionally emphasized the impact of erosion on productivity, partly building on research results since 1993. The overall objective was to develop (1) economically viable and

technically sound soil conservation technology, and (2) strategies and approaches to enhance adoption amongst smallholders. Consequently, collaboration with farmer groups, nongovernment organizations (NGOs), and national partners was sought and became increasingly important.

Figure 1 illustrates the conceptual framework guiding the project. Technology improvement is seen as a continuum in which scientists, end users, and facilitators form part of the development cycle. Feedback, inputs, and outputs can and have to move in both directions of the development cycle. Collaboration with farmers did not follow a defined or fixed scheme but depended on the questions to be dealt with and on individual situations. Farmer involvement was sought through visits to the research station and to farms, through diagnostic interviews, on-farm demonstration trials, which were farmer- and researcher-managed, and participatory trials (Ashby 1990). Secondary information about the farm situation was also collected from NGOs working in rural development.

Soil Erosion

This project addressed the problem of soil erosion in hillside farming

*   CIAT, Cali, Colombia.
**   Hohenheim University, Stuttgart, Germany.
*** Visiting Researcher at CIAT, now at the Universidad Autónoma de Occidente, Cali, Colombia.

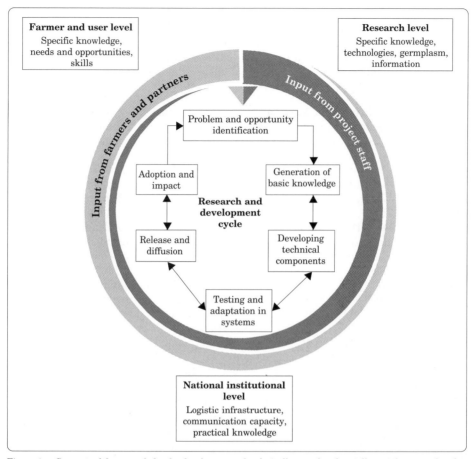

Figure 1.   Conceptual framework for the development of technically sound and socially satisfactory soil and water conservation technology (modified from Henry 1993).

systems. It was assumed that erosion is the main biophysical constraint to sustainability on Andean hillsides. Other problems, such as productivity, diversification, and well-being were subordinated; that is, they were considered only if strong interactions were expected with respect to solving the main constraint.

Evidence from other parts of the world and our own findings supports the hypothesis that soil erosion is a major obstacle to sustainability in tropical hillsides. Worldwide, it accounts for more than 50% of soil destruction. It is further estimated that already 15% of the world's arable

land is strongly or extremely degraded, an area equivalent to twice the croplands of Canada (Gardner 1996). Despite such losses, deterioration of arable lands continues at increasing levels. Whereas between 1945 and 1990, annual losses averaged 2 million hectares, some sources suggest that today's losses are higher than 5 million hectares per year (Scherr and Yadav 1996).

Growing cassava under marginal conditions is contributing to this trend (Castillo F and Müller-Sämann 1996; CIAT 1993). Because cassava is one of CIAT's mandated crops, specific attention was given to the problem in cassava-based systems. As research in the southern Colombian Andes revealed, on a typical cassava field, soil losses varied from 30 to 130 t/ha per year, depending on rainfall characteristics (Table 1).

On shallow hillside soils, losses at this order of magnitude can affect yield potential in a relatively short period of time. The removal of only 5 cm of topsoil reduces cassava root yield by 43% (from 16 to 9.1 t/ha) and removing 10 cm of topsoil reduces yield by 79% (from 16 to 3.4 t/ha). The reductions could be modeled with high accuracy by a modified productivity index (P_i) (CIAT 1997b; Flörchinger and Müller-Sämann 1996; Pierce et al. 1983).

Measured erosion levels were linked with the model to predict productivity losses, applying conservative lowest levels of erosion observed, over a 6-year period (Table 2). From a historic or macroeconomic viewpoint, productivity losses of 20% in one, and of 60% in two, human generations are dramatic, depriving future generations of the possibility of making a living on these hillsides.

Yet, it is doubtful if these losses are high enough to influence farmers' behavior (Smith et al. 1997). Although soils eroded quickly, yield decline over one active farmer's life remains within the order of variations, which also occur because of biotic or abiotic stresses like pests, diseases, or drought. Moreover, they can be overcome and masked by applying fertilizers. One cannot therefore expect poor farmers to perceive this ecological disaster as a major problem.

Consequently, to assume that fighting erosion is a high farmer priority is to be unrealistic, an assumption corroborated by the findings of a diagnostic survey of 66 cassava farmers in the Department of Cauca in southern Colombia. Although nearly all farmers had observed that heavy rains remove soil and over 95% said that soil erosion leads to lower yields, only 13% included decline of soil fertility among major production problems. Erosion ranked far behind water and water quality, market development for better incomes, and lack of technical assistance (CIAT 1995).

Suggested Solutions

Unsurprisingly, farmer adoption of the technology for soil conservation was minimal and only occurred to a significant extent when the project team supplied seedlings and helped with planting.

Undersowing with forage legumes

Undersowing with soil-covering forage legumes that could be fed to small ruminants and cattle offers potential

Table 1. Soil losses in sole cassava cropping systems on an Oxic Dystropept, standardized to a 25% slope, 50 m long, Colombian Andes.

Sole cassava crop	Soil losses per year (t/ha)					
	1987/88	1988/89	1990/91	1991/92	1992/93	1993/94
Traditional	38.3	129.0	62.0	36.8	34.5	56.3
With grass barriers[a]	39.8	114.8	12.8	12.0	7.5	8.3

a. Barriers every 8 m; unplowed contour strips with native grass (1 m) from 1987 to 1989, or planted vetiver grass barriers from 1990 to 1994.

Table 2. Productivity losses over 6 years, calculated with the modified productivity index, as a consequence of soil erosion in sole cassava cropping, Colombia[a].

Duration of cassava cropping (years)	Productivity loss[b] (%)
5	2.5
10	4.8
20	11.1
30	19.1
50	39.3
70	65.8

a. On an Andean Inceptisol with a 25% slope.
b. Reduction of yield, caused by loss of soil at a rate of 34.5 t/y.

short-term benefits to farmers and was considered as a soil conservation technology by researchers. Fast-covering forage species like *Chamaecrista rotundifolia* (CIAT accession no. 8990) were found to be adapted to local conditions, but could not be introduced as a viable option for farmers because:

1. Erosion control in the year of establishment is minimal.

2. Yields of the main crop are affected, or the risk of low yield becomes high with irregular rainfall.

3. No sowing equipment for hillside farmers exists, which makes undersowing labor intensive.

4. The need for forages, or scarcity of land in the project area, is not so pressing as to justify a relatively sophisticated and costly means of cultivation and harvest.

The technology could not be further developed to a stage where it had a reasonable chance of success on the farm. These conclusions were also reached after dialog with farmers who visited the research station.

Barrier technology

Another practice for reducing levels of soil erosion is to plant grass barriers (Table 1). The technology is simple and is often recommended to hillside farmers. Grasses screened for adaptability to acid, low fertility hillsides and recommended to farmers included vetiver (*Vetiveria zizanioides*), dwarf elephant (*Pennisetum purpureum* cv. Mott), citronella (*Cymbopogon nardus*), and imperial grass (*Axonopus scoparius*). Farmers planted these grasses in demonstration trials.

Planting and maintenance of grass barriers, however, also involves labor and other costs (Table 3). Under conditions prevailing in the Department of Cauca, 3 weeks of labor and US$103 were required to establish 1000 linear meters of grass barriers per hectare. Once established, they still required about 5 days labor per hectare per year for maintenance.

Various authors (Bechstedt 1997; CIAT 1997a; Fujisaka 1993; Müller-Sämann 1997a) mention reasons for the low adoption rates of the barrier technology by small-scale farmers.

Table 3. Costs of establishing 1000 linear meters of citronella grass (*Cymbopogon nardus*) barriers per hectare at 1997 prices, Department of Cauca, Colombia.

Activity	Labor (days)	Cost (US$)
Soil preparation	2.6	21
Establishment (planting)	7.0	42
Maintenance (2 cuts per year)	5.2	40
Total first year	14.8	103

These are:

1. The technology is often applied prematurely with deficiencies;

2. Technical assistance and/or follow-up is missing;

*3. The technology shows monodisciplinary characteristics, and is isolated;

*4. Users are not involved in technology development or selection;

*5. The technology does not respond to farmer priorities;

*6. The technology is not economically attractive;

*7. Absence of integrated approaches; and

8. Lack of a favorable political and institutional environment.

In a situation with no or only extensive cattle raising and largely unsatisfied basic needs, the barrier technology faces the five asterisked obstacles.

Integrated Novel Strategies to Overcome Adoption Constraints

Strategy A: adding value to a technically viable option

Citronella grass in barriers for erosion control constitutes a simple and effective technology to reduce soil losses on low fertility hillsides. The grass contains an essential oil that is widely commercialized for use in scented candles, perfumes, and household cleaners. Extracting and selling the oil would add value to the conservation component. A funding request was submitted to the Deutsche Gesellschaft für Technische Zusammenarbeit (GTZ; the "German Agency for Technical Cooperation" in English) to finance a small oil-extraction factory for a group of rural women. This activity was undertaken by a regional NGO (Fundación para la Investigación y el Desarrollo Agrícola [FIDAR]) in close collaboration with the project and women's group, Asociación de Mujeres Campesinas del Pital (AMCAPI).

The idea of earning cash from the conservation component sharply increased adoption rates and, within 1 year, farmers planted more than 25 km of citronella hedgerows. After 4 years, the factory is still functioning and the oil is sold to regional, small-scale clients. After paying for labor to cut the grass and for fuel, however, net gains resulted in only moderate income generation. Activities are needed to add more value through elaboration of products derived from citronella oil (e.g., scented candles, bio-cleaners). Some are already produced with promising prospects at local markets.

Although this approach was successful it also became clear that the strategy is limited because of small domestic markets for the oil and oil-derived products and because of a relatively high capital investment for which a donor is not always available. Also, constructing and operating a factory in a marginal environment was difficult and required high investment in human resource development, and the competence and dedication of the local NGO. The capacity to cover large areas by this technology is thus limited.

Strategy B: developing and optimizing a local opportunity

A different strategy was followed in the case of broom grass (*Leptocoryphium lanatum*), which grows in scattered

80

patches on fallowed hillside lands of low fertility. Farmers in Buenos Aires, Cauca, harvest the grass, then dry, pack, and sell it to craftsmen for manufacturing brooms. We had been visiting farmers to discuss the growing of fodder grasses and vetiver hedgerows on their sloping cassava fields. But the farmers did not own cattle, making our recommendation useless. But we saw broom grass, locally known as *partiña*, a plant that could be developed as a soil conservation component with potentially higher levels of adoption because it was already being used.

In agronomic on-station evaluation and on-farm trials, the grass was tested for its ease of transplanting, capacity to tiller, productivity, and effectiveness in a barrier. A recommendation for its use in a soil-conserving barrier arrangement was developed and implemented on one farmer's field. The strategy was to cultivate the grass in soil-conserving strips, making for easy harvesting instead of the previous labor-intensive collection on fallow land.

In parallel, a small pilot plant for manufacturing brooms was established. An economic *ex ante* analysis of production of the raw material in barriers and of broom fabrication was conducted. Both were highly profitable with grass production giving a net salary of US$12 a day and broom manufacturing yielding a daily salary of US$20—about three times what a laborer can obtain in this region. Because of low investments for the processing unit, the internal rate of return was as high as 633%, indicating a minimal risk for broom manufacturing.

The bottleneck for the technology, however, will be market volume. Assuming 5% of urban households in the nearby city of Cali (2 million inhabitants) would buy one broom per year, the area needed to produce the raw material would not exceed 10 to 15 ha. Although a viable solution could be developed with a small group of farmers, this clearly is far too low an amount to generate the environmental impact required to reverse the trends of degradation in this region.

Strategy C: optimizing environmental performance of an introduced component based on market opportunities

Market perspectives (volumes and relatively low risks) were taken as the principal starting point for developing another soil conservation technology. This work went forward in collaboration with CIAT projects on rural agroindustries and community management of watershed resources.

Studies of local, regional, and national markets revealed that blackberry (*Rubus glaucus*) constitutes an excellent small-scale farmer crop, which uses family labor and has a stable and increasing demand in Colombia. Milk was also identified as another market opportunity in this region; and better pastures were needed to increase milk production.

Blackberry is typically grown as a sole plantation crop. If the surface between the plants is covered with grasses and weeds, with only a plate around the plant kept free of vegetation, it is a sustainable crop for hillsides. However, an arrangement in "productive-protective strips" with cut-and-carry forage can increase the area protected by a factor of between 4 and 8, depending on the distance between strips. This system was promoted and proposed.

Farmer adoption of the blackberries was excellent. Although no subsidies were given, credit was provided at commercial interest rates.

The adoption of the "productive-protective strips", combined with mulch/forage barriers was much less, however, and will require additional educational efforts.

The project decided to evaluate different arrangements (sole crop, sole blackberry, combined blackberry and grass strips with crops) in participatory trials with five families. Farmers were helped to evaluate the systems with respect to productivity, quality, soil loss, and labor requirements so they could make decisions based on their own experiences. Although total production is much higher with this approach, and areas are potentially protected with a system that should optimize economic and environmental benefits (Müller-Sämann 1997b), the areas protected have remained limited. Enough blackberries can be produced in an area equivalent to 10 to 20 municipalities to saturate national markets.

Strategy D: developing an integrated systems approach for transforming cropping systems

Grass/legume ley was introduced into the traditional rotations of cassava, maize, and cowpea or beans. Vigorous legumes, such as _Centrosema macrocarpum_ (CIAT accession no. 5713), adapted to acid, low fertility soils, were combined with grasses such as _Brachiaria decumbens_ to replace traditional bush fallows. This combination was able to open up the soil and subsoil and to restore favorable physical soil characteristics. When used as a fallow, excellent performance of subsequently cropped cassava could be observed, both with and without tillage, leaving a mulch layer at the surface after spraying the grass with a herbicide.

Grass/legume mixtures applied over 2 years produced forage yields of between 20 and 25 tons of dry matter per hectare. High forage and crop yield on the one hand (Table 4) and minimal soil losses on the other led to a "win-win" situation with economic and environmental benefits at a higher intensity of land use.

The intensive grass/legume rotation not only decreased erosion but was also effective against other forms of soil degradation associated with conventional land use. Structural stability, infiltration rates, soil compaction, and soil organic matter content could be improved (data not included). The 2-year-old grass/legume mixtures enabled farmers to shift successfully to minimum tillage (Table 4), a highly soil-conserving technology (Castillo F and Müller-Sämann 1996; Derpsch, 1995; Müller-

Table 4. Influence of cropping sequences on soil loss and cassava root yield in Santander de Quilichao, Department of Cauca, Colombia.

Proceeding 2 years of cropping treatment	Subsequent crop	Soil loss (t/ha)	Cassava root yield (t/ha fresh roots)
Cassava	Cassava, tillage	5.2	16.9
Weed fallow	Cassava, tillage	0.8	20.6
Grass/legume[a]	Cassava, minimum tillage	0.5	26.4
Grass/legume[b]	Cassava, tillage	0.6	26.7
LSD$_{0.05}$	-	3.8	6.7

a. Legume left after cassava/legume mixture, grass interplanted.
b. Planted simultaneously in tilled soil.

Sämann and Castillo F 1997). To implement the system with farmers, about 50% of land has to be set aside for grass/legume mixtures and farmers need to adopt more intensive animal husbandry. Only on this basis can they make best use of the ley and improve the value of the grass/legume ley.

Permanent minimum tillage is also a promising technology, although it still requires the identification of species that will produce enough mulch *in situ* in relay crops or rotations. Sowing equipment might also be helpful and needs to be developed for interplanting grasses and legumes in the hillsides.

Studies (CIAT 1995) revealed that more than 40% of farmers in the area see the best opportunities in animal husbandry. More than 50% of the land is in fallow or extensive pastures, indicating a high probability of success of ley rotation or minimum tillage systems. The technology therefore merits efforts in grass and legume germplasm for acid soils, local development institutions, and farmers. Contrary to previous recommendations, conservation in this approach does not depend on markets, agroindustries, or on what farmers are producing, but is a result of production methods. In this respect, the potential impact of the technology is unlimited and in a sense unique.

Conclusions

A combined effort of on-station, laboratory, and on-farm research is required to come up with sound and viable soil conservation strategies. Both users and investigators need to be stimulated to reach attractive and feasible solutions for soil and water conservation.

Participatory research at an early stage of technology development is a highly efficient methodology to stimulate dialog and the flow of information between researchers and farmers. It also increases research efficiency, complementing on-station work. Integrated approaches that consider development, income generation, and sustainable resource management have a high potential for adoption. Efficient mechanisms of collaboration will lead to needed knowledge of multiple stakeholders and disciplines.

The impact of conservation technology, developed considering market opportunities and added value to conservation components, is often limited in area. Technologies such as ley farming (grassland/crop rotation) and minimum tillage merit special attention because of their potential for sustainability and to cover large areas.

References

Ashby J. 1990. Evaluating technology with farmers: a handbook. Investigación Participativa en Agricultura/ *Participatory Research in Agriculture* (IPRA), CIAT, Cali, Colombia. 95 p.

Bechstedt HD. 1997. Some socioeconomic and policy conditions affecting sustainable land management in a northern Thai village. IBSRAM (Int Board Soil Resour Manage) Newsl 44:4-5.

Castillo F, JA; Müller-Sämann K. 1996. Conservación de suelos en ladera: Buscando nuevas alternativas. In: Proc. Seminario nacional sobre actualización en conservación de suelos en ladera. Centro de Estudios para la Conservación Integral de la Ladera (CECIL), Bogotá, Colombia. p 87-106.

CIAT. 1993. Cassava Program annual report. Working document no. 146. Cali, Colombia. p 173-198.

CIAT. 1995. Diagnóstico sobre condiciones socioeconómicas y de manejo de recursos naturales en una zona yuquera del norte del Departamento del Cauca. Soil Conservation, Special Project, working document no. 1. Cassava Program, CIAT, Cali, Colombia. 28 p.

CIAT. 1997a. Cassava Program annual report 1994 and 1995. Working document no. 168. Cali, Colombia. p 186-199.

CIAT. 1997b. Project PE-5 Sustainable Systems for Smallholders, annual report 1997. TD 42-52. Cali, Colombia.

Derpsch R. 1995. Rotación de cultivos. In: Siembra directa. Ministerio de Agricultura y Ganadería, Asunción, Paraguay. p 70-107.

Flörchinger F; Müller-Sämann K. 1996. El efecto de la erosión en la productividad del suelo. In: Proc. Seminario nacional sobre actualización en conservación de suelos en ladera. Centro de Estudios para la Conservación Integral de la Ladera (CECIL), Bogotá, Colombia. p 131-136.

Fujisaka S. 1993. A case of farmer adaptation and adoption of contour hedgerows for soil conservation. Exp Agric 29:97-105.

Gardner G. 1996. Shrinking fields: cropland loss in a world of eight billion. Worldwatch paper, no. 131. Worldwatch Institute, Washington, DC. 55 p.

Henry G, ed. 1993. Trends in CIAT commodities, 1993. Working document no. 128. Cali, Colombia. 221 p.

Müller-Sämann K. 1996. Diagnóstico socioeconómico y de manejo de recursos naturales en veredas yuqueras de Santander de Quilichao, norte del departamento del Cauca: Resultados de un trabajo interinstitucional, encuesta realizada el primer trimestre de 1994. Soil Conservation, Special Project, working document no. 2. Cassava Program, CIAT, Cali, Colombia. 33 p.

Müller-Sämann K. 1997a. Hacia conceptos integrales en la conservación de suelos y aguas en la zona Andina. Paper presented at an international workshop on Soil and Water Conservation for the Andean Zone, held at CIAT, 14-17 Oct 1997, Palmira, Colombia.

Müller-Sämann K. 1997b. Propuesta técnica para la producción de mora (*Rubus glaucus*) y de pasto imperial (*Axonopus scoparius*) como componentes de conservación en laderas. Soil Conservation, Special Project, working document no. 3. CIAT and Hohenheim University, Cali, Colombia. 16 p.

Müller-Sämann K; Castillo F, JA. 1997. Labranza mínima, una tecnología para las laderas de Colombia? Conservando 1(1 and 2).

Pierce FJ; Larson WE; Dowdy RH; Graham WAP. 1983. Productivity of soils: assessing long term changes due to erosion. J Soil Water Conserv 38:39-44.

Reining L. 1992. Erosion in Andean hillside farming: characterization and reduction of soil erosion by water in small-scale cassava cropping systems in the southern central cordillera of Colombia. Hohenheim Tropical Agriculture Series no. 1. Verlag Josef Margraf, Weikersheim, Germany. 219 p.

84

Ruppenthal M. 1995. Soil conservation in Andean cropping systems: soil erosion and crop productivity in traditional and forage-legume based cassava cropping systems in the southern Colombian Andes. Hohenheim Tropical Agriculture Series no. 3. Verlag Josef Margraf, Weikersheim, Germany. 110 p.

Ruppenthal M; Leihner DE, Hilger TH; Castillo F, JA. 1996. Rainfall erosivity and erodibility of Inceptisols in the southwest Colombian Andes. Exp Agric 32:91-101.

Scherr S; Yadav S. 1996. Land degradation in the developing world: implications for food, agriculture, and the environment to 2020. Food, Agriculture and Environment Discussion Paper no. 14. International Food Policy Research Institute (IFPRI), Washington, DC. 36 p.

Smith J; Cadavid JV; Rincón A; Vera RR. 1997. Land speculation and intensification at the frontier: a seeming paradox in the Colombian savanna. Agric Sys 54:501-520.

CHAPTER 8

Developing Sustainable Cassava Production Systems with Farmers in Asia

R. H. Howeler*

Introduction

Poor farmers grow cassava (*Manihot esculenta* Crantz) in areas with production constraints such as sloping land, poor soils, and low or unpredictable rainfall. The crop is grown in these areas because it is better adapted to unfavorable conditions than are most other crops. Cassava is popular with poor farmers because it is easy to grow, requiring little or no land preparation and no spraying of pesticides. It will also produce better yields than most other crops when grown on poor soils without applying lime or fertilizers.

However, growing cassava on slopes may result in severe erosion; and growing it on infertile soils without fertilizer or manure application can result in soil nutrient depletion. When cassava is grown for many years under such conditions, yields are likely to decrease because of soil degradation due to erosion and nutrient depletion. This has been clearly demonstrated in fertilizer trials conducted on farmers' fields in northeastern Thailand (Sittibusaya 1993). During 25-35 years of experimentation, cassava yields decreased from 26-29 t/ha to about 10-12 t/ha when the crop was grown

without fertilizer application in three different soil series (Howeler 1995).

Research has shown that cassava does not extract more nutrients from the soil than other crops (Howeler 1991; Putthachroen et al. nd), but that manure or fertilizer (especially K) must be applied to maintain soil fertility when cassava is grown continuously on the same land. When grown on slopes, cassava production may result in more erosion than that of other crops because of its wide spacing and slow initial development, which exposes the soil to direct rainfall (Puttacharoen et al. nd).

However, many crop/soil management practices have been identified that will reduce erosion, such as minimum tillage, planting more closely, fertilizer application, contour ridging, mulching, intercropping, or planting live contour barriers. Some of these practices may also increase yields, and others are likely to reduce yields (contour barriers may take up 10%-20% of the land). Most of these practices will require additional labor or other inputs. Also, because farmers' soils, climatic and socioeconomic conditions, and cropping practices differ from place to place, researchers cannot make recommendations that are widely applicable and acceptable to farmers.

---

* CIAT Regional Office for Asia, Bangkok, Thailand.

To choose the most suitable practices, trade-offs must be considered, and the farmers themselves make these decisions best. To develop technologies that are highly site-specific and require difficult choices, a holistic and participatory approach must be used, where farmers are directly involved in the research and decision making (Howeler 1996).

The Cassava Project in Asia is supported by the Nippon Foundation. The project aims to develop a farmer participatory research (FPR) approach for testing and selecting useful soil and crop management practices that will improve the long-term sustainability of cassava-based cropping systems, and the well-being of cassava farmers. Table 1 lists the national institutes that are collaborating in this project.

Methodology

In Asia, cassava is grown mainly in Thailand, Indonesia, India, China, Vietnam, and the Philippines (in descending order of production). During the first phase of the project (1994-1998), the FPR component was conducted in Thailand, Indonesia, Vietnam, and China. Strategic and applied research was also conducted in these four countries and in the Philippines.

Table 1. Institutions collaborating with CIAT in the Nippon Foundation's project on "Improving Agricultural Sustainability in Asia".

Country, province	Institution	FPR[a] project	Research
China			
Hainan	Chinese Academy of Tropical Agricultural Sciences (CATAS)	✓	✓
Guangxi	Guangxi Subtropical Crops Research Institute (GSCRI)		✓
Guangdong	Upland Crops Research Institute (UCRI)		✓
Indonesia			
East Java	Brawijaya University (UNIBRAW)	✓	✓
	Research Institute for Legumes and Tuber Crops (RILET)	✓	✓
West Java	Bogor Research Institute for Food Crops (BORIF)		✓
Philippines			
Leyte	Philippine Root Crop Research and Training Center (PRCRTC)		✓
Bohol	Bohol Experiment Station (BES)		✓
Thailand			
	Field Crops Research Institute (FCRI), Department of Agriculture (DOA)	✓	✓
	Field Crops Promotion Division, Department of Agricultural Extension (DOAE)	✓	✓
	Thai Tapioca Development Institute	✓	
	Kasetsart University		✓
Vietnam			
Thai Nguyen	Agroforestry College no. 3, Thai Nguyen University (AC#3)	✓	✓
Hanoi	National Soil and Fertilizer Institute (NSFI)	✓	
Ho Chi Minh	Institute of Agricultural Sciences (IAS)		✓

a. FPR = farmer participatory research.

In each of the four countries, the various national institutes selected a team of researchers and extension workers to collaborate in the project. These four teams participated in a training course on FPR methodologies held in July 1994 in Rayong, Thailand.

During 1994, each team conducted rapid rural appraisals (RRAs) in areas potentially suitable as pilot sites for the project. Team members informally interviewed farmers at the sites for information about the biophysical and socioeconomic conditions in the village, the agronomic practices used in cassava production, and the marketing and use of the crop. From the results of these RRAs, two or three pilot sites were selected in each country based on the following criteria:

1. Cassava is, and is likely to remain, an important crop in the area.

2. Cassava is grown on slopes and erosion is a serious problem.

3. Farmers consider erosion a problem and would like to find a solution.

Once the most suitable pilot sites had been identified, researchers established a demonstration field with a range of treatments designed to reduce erosion, and if possible increase yields. The demonstration plots were laid out along contour lines on a uniform slope. Along the lower end of each plot a channel was dug (about 0.4 m wide and 0.4 m deep) and lined with plastic. Eroded soil and runoff water accumulated in these channels. Runoff water was allowed to seep away through small holes made in the plastic, and sediments were collected and weighed. Sediment samples were taken to determine its moisture content and to calculate soil losses on a dry weight basis.

At harvest, farmers from the selected pilot sites were invited to visit these demonstration plots. Farmers heard an explanation about each treatment and saw the growth (or yield) of cassava, and the amount of eroded sediments in the erosion channels. They were asked to score each treatment in terms of usefulness under their own conditions. From these evaluations researchers obtained a better idea about the type of treatments farmers might accept, and the reasons for unacceptability of other management options.

Back in their own village, farmers and FPR team members again discussed the results of the demonstration plot evaluations, and those farmers interested in participating in the project decided among themselves the treatments they considered most useful for testing in trials on their own fields. Farmers usually wanted to test 3 or 4 common treatments to compare with their own traditional practice; in some cases, they also each selected an additional treatment of their own personal interest. These were usually chosen from treatments farmers had seen in the demonstration plots but, in some cases, farmers made their own adaptations. For example, farmers in Thailand substituted hedgerows of king grass with sugarcane, because they could sell the cane at the market.

The FPR team members helped farmers select suitable sites for conducting the trials. For the erosion control trials, the land had to have a uniform slope. Team members set out the contour lines and helped farmers stake out the plots, construct the plastic-lined erosion channels, and establish the treatments. Besides erosion control trials, farmers also established trials testing varieties, fertilizers, and various intercropping systems, to develop a complete package of agronomic practices that would reduce erosion and increase yields or income.

Farmers joining the project were not selected but volunteered to participate. In Vietnam and Thailand, these were both men and women farmers, but in China and Indonesia only men participated in the meetings and selected treatments. During group discussions as part of the RRA, farmers mentioned and sometimes prioritized their problems. Sites were only considered suitable for the project if cassava was a major crop and erosion was considered a serious problem (at least mentioned by the farmers as a problem).

During the crop's development, FPR team members visited the trials regularly to see progress, collect and weigh eroded sediments, and discuss with the farmers any problems that might have occurred. At harvest, a Farmers' Field Day was organized to harvest all the trials. Farmers and FPR team members weighed the harvested roots in each plot, determined their starch content (in Thailand only), and collected and weighed the eroded sediments. The yields of cassava, intercrops, and barrier species were quickly calculated and tabulated. Gross income, production costs, and net income were also calculated and, together with the data on erosion losses, were presented to the farmers. After discussing the results and considering the benefits (increased income and less erosion) and the costs of each treatment, farmers selected the best ones. From these, farmers decided on which to test in the following cycle. In all four countries, two cycles of FPR trials have been completed and the third cycle is in progress.

In Thailand and Vietnam, as part of a field practice during the training-of-trainers (TOT) course in FPR methodologies, trainees conducted a participatory evaluation (PE), in which they asked farmers at the FPR pilot site to define criteria for judging either new varieties or erosion control practices. Each farmer then judged those used in the FPR trials according to their criteria, by distributing a fixed number of beans among the rows and columns of a matrix. This matrix ranking indicated which varieties or practices farmers preferred, and which criteria they considered most important in judging the performance of treatments.

Results and Discussion

Although the FPR teams in each country conducted the project more or less following the above-mentioned steps, they were free to make their own modifications considered more suitable for local conditions. For example, in Thailand, Vietnam, and China, demonstration plots were laid out and managed by researchers at an experiment station. Farmers from the two pilot sites were brought by bus to visit the trials. In Indonesia, two sets of demonstration plots were laid out in farmers' fields at the two pilot sites. The FPR team members and some farmers jointly managed these.

In China, during the first year of FPR trials, many farmers participated, with each having only two treatments—the farmer's traditional and one "improved" practice. The many trials made their supervision by the FPR team more difficult, and comparing each different treatment with the farmer's check complicated the interpretation of results. Therefore, in the second and third year, the number of participating farmers was reduced, and the number of treatments in each trial was increased. Table 2 shows the type and number of

Table 2. Types and number of farmer participatory research (FPR) trials with cassava conducted in four countries in Asia in 1995/96 and 1996/97.

Type of trial	Number of FPR trials								
	Thailand[a]		Vietnam[b]			China[c]		Indonesia[d]	
	1	2	1	2	3	1	2	1	2
1995/96									
Erosion control	9	6	6	7	3	12	-	10	7
Varieties	5	7	6	-	1	15	-	-	8
Fertilization	5	-	4	-	1	10	-	-	-
Intercropping	-	-	8	-	-	-	-	-	-
Total	19	13	24	7	5	37	-	10	15
1996/97									
Erosion control	8	7	5	7	3	4	1	10	9
Varieties	3	6	11	3	3	4	1	1	5
Fertilization	8	-	6	4	3	4	1	1	-
Intercropping	-	-	11	-	-	-	-	-	-
Total	19	13	33	14	9	12	3	12	14

a. Thai sites in (1) Soeng Saang, Nakorn Ratchasima, and (2) Wang Nam Yen, Sra Kaew.
b. Vietnamese sites in (1) Pho Yen District, Thai Nguyen Province, (2) Thanh Hoa District, Phu Tho Province, (3) Loung Son District, Hoa Binh Province.
c. Chinese sites in (1) Baisha and (2) Tunchang, Hainan.
d. Indonesian sites in (1) Dampit, Malang, and (2) Wates, Blitar.

FPR trials conducted at each pilot site of the four countries in 1995/96 and in 1996/97. This paper mainly describes results obtained in Vietnam.

FPR Project in Vietnam: A Case Study

Diagnosis and site selection through RRAs

In Vietnam, the FPR project was executed in collaboration with the Agroforestry College no. 3 (AC#3) of the Thai Nguyen University, Thai Nguyen Province, and with the National Soil and Fertilizer Institute (NSFI), located just outside Hanoi. The AC#3 conducted RRAs in Pho Yen District of Thai Nguyen Province and selected the villages of Dac Son and Tien Phong as suitable sites. These two villages are about 10 km apart and are considered as one pilot site. They are located about 25 km south of Thai Nguyen City. The FPR team of NSFI conducted RRAs in Thanh Hoa District of Phu Tho Province and in Luong Son District of Hoa Binh Province. They selected the village of Kieu Tung, Thanh Hoa District, and the village of Dong Rang, Luong Son District, as the two most suitable sites. Kieu Tung is about 180 km west, and Dong Rang about 60 km southwest, of Hanoi.

Table 3 shows some results of the RRAs conducted at the three pilot sites in Vietnam. The two villages in Pho Yen District have white sandy loam soils of low fertility, a rolling topography, and slopes of 5%-20%. In Kieu Tung Village (Thanh Hoa District), the upland soils are highly acid, red clays of low fertility, and cassava is grown on hillsides with

Table 3. Cropping systems, varieties, and agronomic practices (CVAs) as determined from rapid rural appraisals conducted at four pilot sites for farmer participatory research in Vietnam, 1996/97.

CVAs	Sites[a]			
	Dong Rang	Kieu Tung	Tien Phong	Dac Son
Cropping system[b] – upland	Tea, C + T; C monocult, peanut, maize	C monocult; C + P; tea, peanut, maize	C + P or C + B or 2-y C rotation with 2-y fallow, sweetpotato	C monocult or C/P rotation or C/B, C/SP, sweetpotato
Varieties: Rice			DT 10, DT 13, CR 203	CR 203, DT 10, DT 13
Cassava	CR 203, hybrids from China Vinh Phu, local	DT 10, DT 13, CR 203 Vinh Phu, local	Vinh Phu, Du, Canh Ng	Vinh Phu
Cassava practices				
Planting time	Early Mar	Early Mar	Feb-Mar	Feb-Mar
Planting distances (cm)	100 x 80	80 x 80; 80 x 60	100 x 50	100 x 50
Planting method	Horiz./inclined	Horizontal	Horiz./inclined	Horizontal
Land preparation	Buffalo/cattle	By hand/cattle	Buffalo	Buffalo
Fertilization	Basal	Basal + side[c]	Basal + side[d]	Basal + side[e]
Ridging	Mounding	Flat	Flat	Flat
Mulching	Rice straw	Peanut residues	Peanut residues	Peanut residues
Root chipping	Hand chipper	Knife	Small grater	Small grater
Drying (days)	3-5	3-5	2-4	2-4
Fertilization				
Cassava:				
Pig manure (t/ha)	5	5	3-5	8-11
Urea (kg/ha)	0	50-135	83	83-110
SSP[f] (18% P_2O_5) (kg/ha)	50-100	0	140	0-280
KCl (kg/ha)	0	0	55	0-280

(Continued)

Table 3.   (Continued.)

CVAs	Sites[a]			
	Dong Rang	Kieu Tung	Tien Phong	Dac Son
Rice:				
Pig or buffalo manure (t/ha)	5	0	-	-
Urea (kg/ha)	120-150	80	-	-
Yield (t/ha)				
Cassava	10-12	8-15	8.5	8.7
Rice (per crop)	3.3-4.2	4.2	3.0-3.1	2.7-3.0
Taro	1.9-2.2	-	-	-
Sweetpotato	-	-	8.0	3.3
Peanut	0.8-1.2	0.5-1.1	1.4	1.3
Pigs (kg liveweight per year)	100-120	-	-	-

a. Dong Rang Village, Luong Son District, Hoa Binh Province; Kieu Tung Village, Thanh Hoa District, Phu Tho Province; and Tien Phong and Dac Son Villages, Pho Yen District, Thai Nguyen Province
b. C = cassava; P = peanut; B = black bean; T = taro; SP = sweetpotato; C + P = cassava and peanut intercropped; C/P = cassava and peanut in rotation.
c. Urea applied 2 months after planting.
d. Urea applied when 5-10 cm tall; NPK + farmyard manure applied when 20 cm tall.
e. NPK applied when 30 cm tall; hilling up.
f. SSP = single superphosphate fertilizer.

rather steep slopes of 10%-40%. In these two districts, lowland rice is the main crop, and cassava is an important upland crop. Cassava is usually grown in monoculture or is intercropped with black beans (*Vigna unguiculata*). In Dong Rang (Luong Son District), the soils are also clayey, and are of medium fertility; cassava is grown on slopes of less than 25%. The lowlands are limited and upland crops like cassava, taro, peanut, sweetpotato, and maize, and pigs are the main sources of income. In this District, cassava is grown in monoculture or intercropped with taro (*Colocasia esculenta* L.). At all four sites, cassava is mainly fertilized with 5-10 t/ha of pig manure and, sometimes, with a small additional application of urea, single superphosphate (SSP), and KCl. The crop is weeded twice and harvested during November and December.

Establishment of demonstration plots

Demonstration plots with 17 treatments were established in 1994 on 18%-24% slopes at the AC#3. These plots were replanted in 1995, 1996, and 1997 with minor modifications.

Table 4 shows the results of the demonstration plots and the farmers' preference score in 1996. Without application of fertilizers or manure, yields were unacceptably low. Applying pig manure increased yields from 3.7 to 17.6 t/ha, but applying manure and NPK fertilizers resulted in a further increase to 24.9 t/ha. The highest yield was obtained by applying NPK fertilizers and incorporating crop residues. The latter is important because Vietnamese cassava farmers usually remove all plant parts from the field, using stems and dry leaves as fuel in the kitchen, and green leaves for feeding fish or pigs, practices which lead to soil nutrient depletion and lower yields.

Soil losses were reduced by applying NPK or manure, and by contour ridging or closer spacing. By far the most effective erosion control practice, however, was the planting of hedgerows of vetiver grass (*Vetiveria zizanioides*) alone or in combination with *Tephrosia candida*. Hedgerows of *Tephrosia* alone were not as effective in terms of soil loss as were those of vetiver. Similar results were obtained in 1994 and 1995. Net income was calculated from total gross income and fertilizer/manure costs. Highest net income was obtained by intercropping cassava with peanut, application of NPK, and contour hedgerows of vetiver grass and *Tephrosia*. This last treatment also resulted in low soil loss and most farmers preferred it. Others preferred the more traditional practice of applying farmyard manure (FYM) and NPK, without intercrops or hedgerows, although this produced a slightly lower net income and higher erosion.

Problems encountered in conducting the project were partly in the area of human or institutional relationships and partly technical. In Thailand, the two principal institutes involved, the Department of Agriculture (DOA) and the DOA Extension (DOAE), worked well together at both sites. Farmers' interest and participation were not as good, partly because erosion is not perceived as a serious problem, and partly because the FPR team preferred to bring their own labor force to finish the work quickly rather than wait for the farmers to organize the work. The FPR team did this mainly because of long distances to the pilot sites, difficulties in communication, and lack of participation by local extension workers.

Table 4. Effect of various soil and crop management treatments on cassava yield, gross and net income, and on soil loss caused by erosion when cassava (cv. Vinh Phu) was grown, Vietnam[a], 1996.

Treatments[b]	Cassava yield (t/ha)	Gross income[c]	Fertilizer cost[d]	Net income	Dry soil loss (t/ha)	Farmers preferring treatment[e]
No fertilizer	3.7	1,865	0	1,865	30	0
NPK	15.5	7,750	1195	6,555	25	0
FYM	17.6	8,815	1000	7,815	26	2
NPK + FYM	24.9	12,435	2195	10,240	25	30
NPK, *Tephrosia* as green manure[f]	18.9	9,475	1195	8,280	24	2
NPK, peanut intercrop, *Tephrosia* + vetiver hedgerow	20.6	14,065[g]	1195	12,870	5	28
NPK, contour ridged[h]	21.2	10,590	1195	9,395	18	12
NPK, *Tephrosia* hedgerow	16.6	8,295	1195	7,100	16	5
NPK, *Flemingia* hedgerow	15.3	7,670	1195	6,475	10	1
NPK, vetiver hedgerow	19.1	9,570	1195	8,375	6	10
NPK, black bean intercrop, *Tephrosia* hedgerow	20.9	10,905[g]	1195	9,710	10	2
NPK, green residue incorporated[i]	27.0	13,500	1195	12,305	19	16
No fertilizer, green residue incorporated[i], *Tephrosia* hedgerow	4.9	2,435	0	2,435	18	0
NPK, *Tephrosia*[j] as green manure	21.0	10,500	1195	9,305	21	0
NPK, spacing 0.6 x 0.8 m[k]	22.2	11,090	1195	9,895	19	2

a. Grown on 18%-24% slopes in the farmer participatory research demonstration plots at the Agroforestry College of Bac Thai, Thai Nguyen, Bac Thai.
b. NPK = 60 kg N + 40 P_2O_5 + 120 K_2O per hectare; farmyard manure (FYM) = 10 t/ha of pig manure.
c. Prices per kilogram: cassava fresh roots = 500 dong; peanut dried pods = 5000 dong; black bean dried grain = 6000 dong.
d. Fertilizer costs per kilogram: urea (45% N) = 3000 dong; single superphosphate (17% P_2O_5) = 1000 dong; KCl (60% K_2O) = 2800 dong; pig manure = 100 dong.
e. Number of farmers preferring the treatment.
f. *Tephrosia* (about 6 t/ha) from outside.
g. Yield per hectare: peanut = 750 kg of dried pods; black bean = 80 kg.
h. All other treatments plowed.
i. Green residue removed in all other treatments.
j. *Tephrosia* (about 1.5 t/ha) grown as intercrop between cassava, pulled and mulched at 4 months after planting.
k. All other treatments spaced 1.0 x 0.8 m.

Selection of participating farmers and treatments

Led by one person, usually the village chief, those farmers interested in participating in the FPR trials decided among themselves who would do what type of trial, depending largely on the farmers' interest and the availability of land with uniform slopes for conducting erosion control trials.

Table 2 shows that 56 farmers participated in the project at three pilot sites in Vietnam in 1996/97. They conducted 15 trials on erosion control, 17 on varieties, 13 on fertilization, and 11 on intercropping systems. Treatments for each trial were decided in consultation between FPR team members and participating farmers. For the erosion trials, farmers in Dac Son and Tien Phong villages in Pho Yen District decided to test four "improved" practices, comparing with their own traditional practice, which varied from farmer to farmer. After seeing the results of the first year, farmers modified the treatments to be tested in the second. In Kieu Tung Village, seven farmers with adjacent plots along the same hillside decided to test seven erosion control treatments, with each farmer testing one treatment with two replicates. All plots were managed identically as far as possible. In 1996, these same treatments were repeated with only slight modifications. In Dong Rang Village, farmers and team members selected six treatments in 1995. After observing the results, some treatments were modified in 1996.

Farmer participatory research trials on farmers' fields

The FPR team selected the most appropriate sites on the farms, then helped the farmers set out contour lines, stake out trials, and build plastic-lined erosion channels. The farmers were given planting material of vetiver grass and seed of *Tephrosia candida* for the hedgerows, and peanut or black bean for the intercrop. For the variety trials, they received planting material of the new varieties; and, for the fertilizer trials, those fertilizers to be tested. The team then helped the farmers plant the trials and establish treatments, and left the farmers to manage the trials. Team members visited regularly to see progress, discuss problems, and weigh sediments collected in the erosion channels.

Sediments were weighed once at about 3 months after planting and again at harvest. In this way, the eroded soil accumulated in the channels and farmers could see the effect of treatments on soil loss caused by erosion.

In 1995, the first year of FPR erosion control trials conducted in Pho Yen District, no significant differences occurred in net income among treatments. Soil loss was relatively

Table 5. Average results of five erosion control trials conducted by farmers in Tien Phong and Dac Son Villages of Pho Yen District, Thai Nguyen Province, Vietnam, 1996.

Erosion control trials	Dry soil loss in 1996 (t/ha)	Yield (t/ha)		Gross income	Production costs[c]	Net income	FP[d] (%)
		Cassava[a]	Intercrop[b]	(million dong per hectare)			
Farmer's practice[e]	8.3	11.5	-	6.9	2.2	4.7	0
Tephrosia hedgerows, no ridging, peanut intercrop	6.6	11.0	0.4	8.5	2.3	6.2	0
Vetiver grass hedgerows, no ridging, peanut intercrop	6.3	12.8	0.3	9.1	2.3	6.8	39
Tephrosia hedgerows, contour ridges, peanut intercrop	4.8	12.3	0.3	9.0	2.3	6.7	58
Vetiver + *Tephrosia* hedgerows, no contour ridges, no intercrops	4.2	12.8	-	7.7	1.9	5.7	3

a. Final yield of fresh roots.
b. Dried pods.
c. Includes cost of manure, fertilizers, and peanut seed.
d. FP = percentage of farmers preferring treatment.
e. Monoculture cassava with 15 t/ha of pig manure, 144 kg urea, 107 kg single superphosphate, and 95 KCl kg/ha.

high but was markedly reduced by intercropping with black bean or peanut, especially when combined with hedgerows of vetiver grass. Farmers overwhelmingly preferred the latter treatment and decided to increase the number of treatments with peanut as intercrop and vetiver or *Tephrosia* as hedgerows in the 1996 trials. In 1996, both yields and soil losses were reduced because of drought. Net income was highest when cassava was intercropped with peanut and with hedgerows of vetiver or *Tephrosia* (Table 5). Farmers clearly preferred these treatments, which also resulted in low levels of erosion. Three farmers then decided to plant contour hedgerows of either vetiver or *Tephrosia*, or the two species combined in small areas (about 500 m²) of their cassava fields. Many other farmers planted peanut instead of black bean as an intercrop, both to increase income and reduce erosion. After the peanut harvest, residues

were incorporated into the soil as green manure.

In Kieu Tung Village, dry soil loss on about 40% slope varied from 43-54 t/ha in 1995 and from 25-28 t/ha in 1996 (Table 6). In both years, lowest soil losses and highest net income were observed by intercropping cassava with peanut and planting contour barriers of vetiver grass; this was also the most preferred treatment. Based on this experience, most farmers in Kieu Tung now plant cassava intercropped with peanut.

In Dong Rang Village, similar results were obtained (Table 7). Intercropping with peanut resulted in a higher net income than the traditional practice of intercropping with taro. Intercropping with peanut, NPK application, and hedgerows of vetiver or *T. candida* reduced soil erosion from 43 t/ha in the traditional practice

Table 6. Effect of seven crop management treatments on various factors in an erosion control trial conducted by six farmers, Kieu Tung Village of Thanh Hoa District, Phu Tho Province, Vietnam, 1996.

Treatments[a]	Slope (%)	Yield (t/ha)		Gross income[b, c]	Production costs[b, d]	Net income[b]	Dry soil loss (t/ha)	FP[e] (%)
		Cassava	Peanut					
Cassava (C) monoculture, no fertilizers, no hedgerows	40.5	15.3	-	7.6	2.6	5.0	27.9	0
C + peanut (P), no fertilizers, no hedgerows	45.0	16.8	1.4	15.6	2.8	12.8	27.4	0
C + P, with fertilizers, no hedgerows	42.7	14.6	1.7	15.6	3.7	11.9	28.1	61
C + P, with fertilizers, *Tephrosia* hedgerows	39.7	15.1	0.9	12.1	3.7	8.4	26.6	0
C + P, with fertilizers, pineapple hedgerows	32.2	21.6	1.0	16.0	3.7	12.2	26.9	71
C + P, with fertilizers, vetiver grass hedgerows	37.7	22.0	1.2	16.8	3.7	13.1	25.3	93
C monoculture, with fertilizers, *Tephrosia* hedgerows	40.0	26.2	-	13.1	3.5	9.6	25.5	0

a. All plots received 10 t/ha of farmyard manure; fertilizers = 60 kg N + 40 P_2O_5 + 120 K_2O per hectare.
b. Million dong per hectare.
c. Prices per kilogram: cassava fresh roots = 500 dong; peanut dried pods = 5000 dong.
d. Production costs per hectare: cassava monoculture = 2.60 million dong; peanut intercropping = 0.20 million dong; NPK application = 0.92 million dong; hedgerows = no additional costs.
e. FP = percentage of farmers preferring treatment.

Table 7. Average results of an erosion control trial conducted by three farmers on 16% slope in Dong Rang Village of Luong Son District, Hoa Binh Province, Vietnam, 1996.

Treatments[a]	Yield (t/ha)		Gross income[b, c]	Fertilizer costs[b, c]	Net income[b]	Biomass incorporated[d]	Dry soil loss (t/ha)	Farmers prefer
	Cassava	Intercrop						
Cassava (C) + taro (T), no fertilizers, no hedgerows	9.0	2.3	7.0	0.7	6.2	-	43.1	-
C + T, with fertilizers, vetiver grass hedgerows	13.0	1.8	8.5	1.5	7.0	0.1	19.7	-
C + T, with fertilizers, *Tephrosia candida* hedgerows	14.1	1.8	9.0	1.5	7.5	0.9	15.9	-
C + peanut, with fertilizers, vetiver grass hedgerows	15.7	0.7	11.1	1.5	9.6	1.6	2.4	+
C + peanut, with fertilizers, *Tephrosia candida* hedgerows	14.3	0.7	10.6	1.5	9.1	2.2	4.0	+

a. All plots received 5 t/ha of farmyard manure (FYM); fertilizers = 40 N + 40 P_2O_5 + 80 K_2O; taro or peanut received separately: 7 N + 20 P_2O_5 + 20 K_2O in all treatments.
b. Millions of dong per hectare.
c. Prices (dong per kilogram): cassava fresh roots = 500; taro fresh corms = 1100; peanut dried pods = 5000; FYM = 100; urea (45% N) = 3000; single superphosphate (17% P_2O_5) = 1000; KCl (60% K_2O) = 2200.
d. Dry biomasss from peanut and leaves of hedgerows.

Table 8. Average results of variety trials conducted by farmers in Tien Phong and Dac Son Villages of Pho Yen District, Thai Nguyen Province, Vietnam, 1996.

Variety or line	Cassava yield (t/ha)	Income (million dong per hectare)		FP (%)[c]
		Gross[a]	Net[b]	
Vinh Phu (local)	20.2	12.1	10.1	0
KM 60	22.5	13.5	11.4	33
0MR 25-33-105	21.8	13.1	11.0	33
SM 937-8	20.8	12.5	10.4	0
CM 4955-7	23.8	14.3	12.2	58
SM 981-3	23.3	14.0	11.9	42
SM 1557-3 (KM 95-3)	23.8	14.3	12.2	100

a. Price per kilogram of cassava fresh roots = 600 dong.
b. Cost of application of 10 t farmyard manure + 174 kg urea + 250 kg single superphosphate + 133 kg KCl is 2.1 million dong per hectare.
c. FP = percentage of farmers preferring treatment.

without fertilizers to 2-4 t/ha. Farmers much preferred the latter two treatments. Some farmers have now planted contour hedgerows of *Tephrosia* in their fields. They like *Tephrosia* better than vetiver grass because it can be established more easily (from seed), and the pruned leaves can be used as green manure.

Table 8 shows the average results of FPR variety trials conducted in Pho

Table 9. Matrix ranking (%) of four cassava varieties by farmers of Tien Phong and Dac Son Villages of Pho Yen District, Thai Nguyen Province, Vietnam, according to their own criteria.

Criterion	Cassava variety				Total[a]
	Vinh Phu	KM 60	KM 95-3	CM 4955-7	
Tien Phong					
High yield	6.4	11.1	8.3	5.1	30.9
High starch[b]	3.3	8.9	4.8	1.8	18.8
Good plant type	3.4	5.0	3.8	0	12.2
Good stake storage	4.7	2.7	2.4	1.8	11.6
Good root shape	2.3	3.7	2.3	0	8.3
Low cyanide content	3.1	2.1	2.3	0	7.5
Good eating quality	9.4	0	1.1	0	10.5
Total	32.6	33.5	25.0	8.7	100.0
Dac Son					
High yield	3.6	8.0	16.8	8.8	37.2
High starch[b]	8.0	5.6	6.0	1.6	21.2
Intermediate height	4.0	4.8	5.2	2.4	16.4
Good plant type	2.0	2.4	3.2	1.2	8.8
Thin peel	4.4	5.2	4.8	1.2	15.6
Total	22.0	26.0	36.0	15.2	99.2

a. Numbers are rounded.
b. Dry matter content.

Yen District. The yields of all six improved varieties or breeding lines were all slightly higher than that of the local cultivar Vinh Phu. Farmers particularly liked SM 1557-3 (KM 95-3). During a matrix ranking of varieties, conducted as part of a PE field practice during the TOT course on FPR methodologies, held in September 1997, farmers in Dac Son Village indicated that they preferred KM 95-3 mainly because of its high yield and starch content (Table 9). However, when "eating quality" was included as a selection criterion in Tien Phong Village, farmers continued to rate their local variety Vinh Phu as the best. None of the farmers of the two villages liked CM 4955-7, despite its high yield, mainly because of its low starch content, poor plant type, and poor storability of planting material.

In FPR fertilizer trials conducted at all three pilot sites, highest cassava yields and net income were obtained by applying 60-80 kg N, 0-40 kg P_2O_5, and 80-120 kg K_2O per hectare, in addition to 5-10 t/ha of pig manure. Based on this experience, farmers reduced their application of P and increased that of K. The FPR trials on intercropping systems, conducted in Pho Yen, showed consistently that intercropping with peanut produced a higher net income than intercropping with black bean or planting in monoculture. Farmers also know from the FPR erosion control trials that intercropping with peanut is a highly effective way to reduce erosion. Thus, they overwhelmingly preferred this cropping system and many have now adopted it in their fields.

Solving Technical Problems

Technical problems encountered were mainly related to remoteness of site, lack of transport, or lack of good quality planting material. In Vietnam, China, and Indonesia, planting material of new varieties to be tested by farmers was lacking for use either in the FPR variety trials, or as an incentive to conduct other types of trials. In Thailand, planting material was usually available, but sometimes arrived at the pilot sites when it had not rained enough to plant. Similarly, fertilizers did not always arrive on time to be applied in the fertilizer trials.

The main technical problem was related to measuring erosion. The FPR erosion-control trials were not always laid out along and perpendicular to contour lines; in that case, runoff water would enter or leave through the side borders of the plots. Farmers like plots to be laid out parallel to field borders, roads, or footpaths, so not to waste land. But for reliable measurements of erosion, plots have to be laid out along contour lines, which are not necessarily straight. A second problem is that runoff water coming from fields located above the trial sometimes entered the plots, causing erosion unrelated to the treatments imposed. Diversion ditches or ridges, which should have been dug along the upper side of the trials, were often absent or ineffective. Finally, the plastic used to line the erosion channels was sometimes of inferior quality, poorly installed, or stolen, making reliable measurement of soil loss impossible. Other technical problems included the poor marking of plots, inadequate weed control, varietal mixtures, irregular planting distance, theft of intercrops, and the damage to cassava plants caused by buffaloes. Table 10 gives an evaluation of achievements.

An important factor in achieving farmer interest and active participation is the availability of technologies that are considerably better than current farmer practices. In Thailand, Vietnam, and China, farmers were mainly interested in the testing and multiplication of new varieties, which also served as an incentive for their conducting other FPR trials. In Indonesia, almost no planting material of new varieties was available, and those that were tested were only marginally better than the local ones. In Thailand, planting material of vetiver grass was widely available and farmers already knew its effectiveness in controlling erosion. In Vietnam, the use of *T. candida* was already well known, but vetiver grass was unknown and planting material was initially not available. In China and Indonesia, no management options were highly attractive or clearly superior to the current practices. Vetiver grass was shown to be effective in reducing erosion, but enough planting material was only available in the second or third year. The lack of really good alternative options reduced farmers' interest and participation.

Successes and Failures

Table 10 summarizes the conditions in which the FPR projects were being conducted in the four countries. Conditions varied markedly in terms of institutional arrangements and interest of FPR team members, distance to the pilot sites (which influenced the frequency of visits by team members), and the interest of local farmers and their leaders.

Cassava was the principal crop only at the site in Soeng Saang District, Thailand, and in Malang District, Indonesia. Slopes were relatively steep in Thanh Hoa District, Vietnam; intermediate in Indonesia,

Table 10. Conditions of farmer participatory research (FPR) trials conducted at eight pilot sites in Asia[a].

Conditions	Thailand			Vietnam		China	Indonesia	
	1	2	3	4	5	6	7	8
Institution[b]	DOA + DOAE	DOA + DOAE	AC#3	NSFI	NSFI	CATAS	RILET	UNIBRAW
Distance (hours)	4-5	4-5	1	3	1	1.5	1	1.5
Participating farmers (no.)	19	13	29	13	9	15	10	14
Principal crop	Cassava	Maize	Rice	Rice	Rice	Rubber	Cassava	Maize
Slope (%)	<10	<20	<15	<40	<30	<30	<30	<20
Erosion (t/ha)[c]	4.3-24.8	18.1-47.8	8.3-29.5	27.9-53.7	9.9-43.1	47.1-125.0	11.8-144.6	27.4-55.0
Type of trial	Erosion, varieties, fertilizer	Erosion, varieties	Erosion, varieties, fertilizer, intercrop	Erosion, varieties, fertilizer	Erosion, varieties	Erosion, varieties, fertilizer	Erosion, varieties, fertilizer	Erosion, varieties
Farmer participation	+	+	+++	+	+	++	+	++
Local leadership	++	++	+++	+	+	++	+	++
Local project responsibility	Village head	Village head	Students	Agronomist	Model farmer	Extension worker	Model farmer	Model farmer
Preferred treatment[d]	Vetiver, sugarcane	Vetiver	Vetiver, C + P	Vetiver, C + P	Tephrosia, C + P	C + P	?	Gliricidia sepium
Technique adopted	New variety, vetiver/ sugarcane	New variety, vetiver	C + P	C + P	C + P	New variety	None yet	None yet
Problems[e]	Distance	Distance	NOP	Distance	NOP	Lack of transport + FGOs	FGOs	FGOs

a. Sites: 1 = Soeng Saang; 2 = Wang Nam Yen; 3 = Luong Son; 4 = Pho Yen; 5 = Thanh Hoa; 6 = Baisha; 7 = Blitar; 8 = Malang.
b. For explanation of acronyms of institutions responsible for trials, see "Acronyms and Abbreviations Used in the Text", pages 161-165.
c. Average dry soil loss under "farmers' practice" in FPR erosion trials in 1995/96 and 1996/97.
d. C + P = cassava intercropped with peanut.
e. Every site had problems with erosion measurements; NOP = site had no other problems; FGOs = few good options.

China, and Luong Son District of Vietnam; and gentle in Thailand and Pho Yen District, Vietnam. Despite the gentle slopes in Thailand, erosion can be severe because of large fields and long slopes. Data on erosion in Table 10 indicate that soil losses varied markedly from year to year, depending mainly on the amount of rainfall received. Soil losses of more than 100 t/ha per year were measured in Malang (Indonesia) and Baisha (China). Soil losses were less on the gentler slopes in Thailand and in Pho Yen District of Vietnam.

In Vietnam, the two institutes, AC#3 and NSFI, worked at their respective sites, independently of each other. The AC#3 team consisted of four researchers and various students; the latter spent a lot of time helping farmers conduct the trials. The relatively short distance to the pilot sites facilitated regular visiting and the establishment of excellent relations with local extension workers and farmers.

In China, only the Chinese Academy of Tropical Agricultural Sciences (CATAS) was actively involved in the project, but lacked both personnel and transport to supervise the trials adequately. Trials in the Kongba Village of Baisha County improved over time as both farmers and the local extension workers gained experience. However, attempts to set up FPR trials at a second site have failed so far, mainly because of lack of personnel and transport, and lack of interest by local extension workers.

In Indonesia, the two institutes involved in the project, the Research Institute for Legumes and Tuber Crops (RILET) and Brawijaya University (UNIBRAW), also worked at their respective sites, independently of each other. These trials have not been successful mainly because of lack of personnel and experience. Basically,

one M.S. student manages the Blitar site and a researcher and a technician manage the Malang site. Especially at the Malang site, real participation by farmers in decision making remains lacking.

Conclusions

Technologies that will increase the sustainability of cassava-based cropping systems were developed in collaboration with national cassava researchers, extension workers, and farmers at nine pilot sites in four Asian countries. Farmers conducted FPR trials on methods to reduce erosion, on varieties, fertilizer practices, and intercropping systems. According to the results of these trials they selected the varieties and management practices most suitable for their own conditions. The preferred technologies included the following:

1. Varieties with high yield, high starch content, and good plant type;

2. Fertilization, mostly with N and K, combined with FYM if available;

3. Intercropping with peanut (Vietnam and China), pumpkin (Thailand), or maize (Indonesia); and

4. Planting contour hedgerows of vetiver (Thailand, Vietnam), sugarcane (Thailand), *T. candida* (Vietnam), or *Gliricidia sepium* (Indonesia).

The project was most successful in those areas where cassava was a highly important crop and where erosion was serious, pilot sites were not too distant, and FPR team members and local extension workers showed enthusiasm for the project. The prior identification of highly promising alternative management options is a prerequisite for achieving farmers' interest and active participation.

To have any significant impact, the project should now expand to other pilot sites and other countries. This can only be done by training more researchers and local extension workers in FPR approaches and methodologies. In Thailand and Vietnam, this process has already started. Institute directors and other "decision makers", and local nongovernment organizations also need to be informed about the FPR approach, to gain their support in enhancing farmer participation in decision making and in the future development of technologies.

References

Howeler RH. 1991. Long-term effect of cassava cultivation on soil productivity. Field Crops Res 26:1-18.

Howeler RH. 1995. Agronomy research in the Asian Cassava Network - towards better production without soil degradation. In: Howeler RH, ed. Cassava breeding, agronomy research and technology transfer in Asia. Proc. 4th Regional Workshop, Nov 2-6, 1993, Trivandrum, Kerala, India. p 368-404.

Howeler RH. 1996. The use of farmer participatory research methodologies to enhance the adoption of soil conservation practices in cassava-based cropping systems in Asia. In: Sombatpanit S; Zobish MA; Sanders DW; Cook MG, eds. Soil conservation extension—from concepts to adoption. Proc. International Workshop on Soil Conservation Extension, June 4-11 1995, Chiang Mai, Thailand. p 159-168.

Putthacharoen S; Howeler RH; Jantawat S; Vichukit V. nd. Nutrient uptake and soil erosion losses in cassava and six other crops in Psamment in eastern Thailand. Field Crops Res (in press).

Sittibusaya C. 1993. Progress report of soil research on fertilization of field crops. Paper presented at the 1992 Annual Cassava Program Review, Jan 19-20, 1993, Rayong, Thailand. (Typescript, in Thai.)

CHAPTER 9

Developing Forage Technologies with Smallholders in East Kalimantan, Indonesia[1]

Werner Stür* and Peter Horne**

Introduction

The Forages for Smallholders Project (FSP) is a 5-year (1995-1999) Southeast Asian regional project, funded by the Australian Agency for International Development (AusAID) and managed by CIAT in collaboration with the Commonwealth Scientific and Industrial Research Organisation (CSIRO). The project focuses on developing forage technologies in partnership with smallholder farmers in upland areas where forages are needed for livestock feeding and resource management (including erosion control, soil fertility improvement, weed control, and reducing labor requirements).

Participatory approaches to technology development are becoming widely used in rural development, but are new to forage technology development in Southeast Asia. In 1995, with the help of the Investigación Participativa en Agricultura (IPRA) at CIAT, the FSP introduced into the region farmer participatory research (FPR) methods, which it has subsequently tested, modified, and implemented. With reference to a particular site in East Kalimantan, this paper describes the learning process that has been taking place in the FSP as it moves toward more active farmer participation in the development of forage technologies.

Background

The FSP is a network of smallholders, development workers, and researchers. It is coordinated by national organizations in southern China, Indonesia, Lao PDR, Malaysia, the Philippines, Thailand, and Vietnam. In partnership with the national coordinating agencies, FSP staff identified sites where local development workers are willing to work with farmers in developing new technologies. Local government agencies or community development projects, both government and nongovernment organizations, employ the development workers. Research sites were selected to cover a range of environments and farming systems, commonly found in upland agriculture in Southeast Asia (Table 1). In 1997, the FSP worked at 17 on-farm sites in Indonesia, Lao PDR, the Philippines, and Vietnam (Figure 1).

1. A summary of ideas found in this paper appears in W. W. Stür's "Developing forage technologies with farmers—an update of activities of the Forages for Smallholders Project". In: *Seafrad News* 6:5, December 1997.

* Forages for Smallholders Project, CIAT, Manila, Philippines.

** Forages for Smallholders Project, Commonwealth Scientific and Industrial Research Organisation (CSIRO),Vientiane, Lao PDR.

Table 1. Predominant agroecosystems at Forages for Smallholders Project (FSP) sites in Southeast Asia.

FSP sites	Agroecosystem[a]					
	G	ISU	ESU	S&B	RFL	P
Indonesia						
Gorontalo, North Sulawesi						✓
Makroman, East Kalimantan		✓				
Marenu, South Tapanuli		✓	✓			
Pulau Gambar, North Sumatra					✓	
Saree, Aceh	✓					
Sepaku II, East Kalimantan	✓		✓			
Lao PDR						
Luang Phabang			✓	✓		
Xieng Khouang				✓		
Philippines						
Cagayan de Oro, Mindanao			✓			
M'lang and Carmen, North Cotabatu			✓		✓	
Davao						✓
Guba, Cebu		✓				
Malitbog, Bukidnon			✓			
Matalom, Leyte		✓	✓			
Vietnam						
Xuan Loc, Hue						
M'Drak, Daklak	✓					
Ha Giang and Tuyen Quang			✓			

a. G = grassland; ISU = intensive sedentary upland; ESU = extensive sedentary upland; S&B = slash and burn; RFL = rainfed lowland; P = plantation.

Additional sites will become operational in Lao PDR and Vietnam in 1998.

Before evaluating forages with farmers, the FSP conducted regional forage evaluation trials. Researchers usually controlled these, sometimes conducted on research stations, sometimes on farmers' fields. The information from these regional evaluations, together with local information, defined the range of forages that could be offered to farmers for evaluation. Regional and on-farm evaluations were and are supported by two sites in the Philippines and Lao PDR that produce seed and vegetative planting material. Planting material

has also been made available to farmers from regional evaluation sites. Other support services include training of national partner staff in FPR, forage agronomy, seed production and supply methodologies, and the development of information systems.

Makroman: A Case Study in FPR

Site description

Makroman is located in the subdistrict of Samarinda Ilir, about 20 km (5 km of unpaved road) from Samarinda, East Kalimantan (0.5° S). The area is a

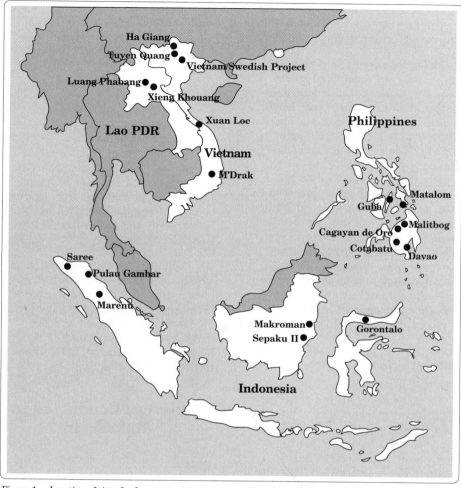

Figure 1.   Location of sites for farmer participatory research and/or participatory technology development carried out by the Forages for Smallholders Project in Southeast Asia.

mixture of lowlands (60%) and hilly uplands (40%), which are dominated by the grass *Imperata cylindrica*. Soils vary from moderately fertile to infertile clay loams with a pH of 4.8 to 5.3. Altitude is less than 100 m above sea level. Average annual rainfall is about 2000 mm, with peak rainfall during December to March and the dry season during June to October.

Makroman is in a transmigration area that Javanese farmers settled in 1974. Land holdings vary from 2-3 ha per family. Most families own 1-2 ha of lowland and 1 ha of upland. Farmers

can usually grow two rice crops per year in the lowland areas. Farmers grow maize and baby corn, cassava, sweetpotatoes, and peanuts on their upland areas, and maintain intensive home gardens with fruit trees and vegetables. Not all upland areas are planted with crops; often only 0.2-0.4 ha are planted and the remainder is dominated by *I. cylindrica*. Some farmers continuously crop the same area with inputs of manure; others practice a crop-fallow system. Farmers are mainly limited in cropping all their upland areas by lack of labor for land preparation and weeding, and declining soil fertility with continuous cropping.

Many families have as many as three cattle and some families also keep 5 to 10 goats. Cattle tend to be kept in stalls or tethered near houses during the night and morning, and are tethered in the farmer's own fields in the afternoon. Farmers cut naturally occurring grasses (including *I. cylindrica*) anywhere in the village area to provide supplementary feed for their animals. Farmers spend 2-4 h per day cutting and carrying feed for their animals. Rice straw or stubble after harvesting belong to the owner. No free grazing of animals occurs. Goats are kept in pens and are usually fed grasses, cassava leaves, jackfruit, *Gliricidia sepium*, and, in the dry season, banana leaves and stems.

Site selection

The Forage Seeds Project (1992-1994), FSP's predecessor, conducted forage species evaluations at several sites in East Kalimantan. Thus, the FSP had a range of well-adapted forage germplasm available for farmer testing. The sites used for this regional evaluation, however, were not suitable for farmer testing because their selection was based mainly on environmental considerations and availability of staff to conduct these experiments.

Makroman was selected as a potential on-farm site based on secondary information and field visits in early 1995. The reasons for selection of the area were:

1. It had been a recipient area for a cattle distribution project.

2. Many farmers had cattle.

3. Organized livestock farmers' groups existed.

4. Farmers and development workers had a good relationship.

5. Animal health services were available to farmers.

6. A local livestock officer was active.

7. The development workers perceived a need for planted forages.

Several other sites were rejected at this stage, mainly because of few potential adopters in the area, lack of need for forages (as perceived by the researchers), and the absence of local livestock officers.

The initial selection of Makroman was made in early 1995. Following introduction of FPR methods to our Indonesian partners, a participatory diagnosis (PD) confirmed selection of Makroman as a promising FPR site in May 1996. A summary of the results of this PD is given later.

Activities Conducted in Makroman

1995

Immediately following preliminary site selection in early 1995, the "Maju" farmer group established small plots of the six best forage species from the previous regional evaluations in East Kalimantan. These included four grasses for cut-and-carry, grazing, and the herbaceous legumes *Stylosanthes guianensis* CIAT 184 and *Centrosema pubescens* CIAT 15160. The development workers decided which species to include in the evaluation and the layout of the plots. The farmers planted and managed the forages and cut them regularly to feed to their animals or allowed them to graze the plots. The area also served as a source of vegetative planting material for farmers wishing to evaluate forages on their own land. Farmers tended to select grasses that are easy to propagate from cuttings. Seven farmers planted small areas of grasses for cut-and-carry and grazing on their farms.

1996

Regional evaluation. In early 1996, following the suggestion of development workers, the "Maju" farmer group established a larger range of 16 forage species in the communal nursery. This experiment was part of a new regional evaluation of forages by the FSP. The development workers suggested the layout of the experiment. Farmers planted, managed, and used the forages within certain guidelines (e.g., minimum cutting height). Farmers and development workers evaluated the experiment, each using their own criteria. Later, participatory evaluation methods were used to better understand farmer selection of forages. This area also served as a source of planting material for farmers wanting to test forages on their own land.

Participatory diagnosis. In May 1996, a PD was organized with members of the "Maju" (22 families owning 45 cattle and about 100 goats). In the 1980s, many members of this farmer group had been recipients of cattle during the ADB II livestock distribution project. Several farmers from a second farmer group, "Sidodadi", also attended the PD. These farmers had seen the new forages at Sidodadi and were interested in being included in project activities. Their members raise only goats, and many had no access to lowland areas. Thirty-three farmers participated in the PD. Men dominated the session, although several women were present. Women were more active during later planning sessions and forage

evaluation on farms. Even so, members of the "Sidodadi" farmer group tended to stay in the background.

The day before the PD, we discussed the farming and livestock systems with a small group of farmers and government representatives to gain a basic understanding of the agricultural systems in the area. During the PD, farmers:

1. Drew maps of their village with roads, houses, and agricultural land;

2. Produced seasonal calendars including rainfall, crop production cycles, labor requirements, and feed supply and sources;

3. Discussed their crop and animal production systems;

4. Listed major problems relating to crop and livestock production;

5. Discussed and prioritized problems; and

6. Discussed causal linkages among problems.

The farmers decided to discuss problems relating to crop production separately from those relating to animal production. Table 2 presents a list of problems that farmers identified.

Farmers saw *I. cylindrica* as the cause of many of the problems (particularly labor requirements) relating to upland cropping. Farmers coped with these problems by growing only small areas of upland crops, and concentrating more on animal production. The consensus among farmers was that animal feed supply is no problem because sufficient naturally occurring grasses were available. The farmers said that it takes 2 to 4 h per day to cut 40-50 kg of fresh feed (found within 3 km of their houses) to feed

Table 2. Problems identified by farmers during participatory diagnosis (in order of priority) at the case study site of Makroman, East Kalimantan, Indonesia.

Crop production	Animal production
1. The grass *Imperata cylindrica* invading upland cropping areas.	1. Flies and mosquitoes causing diseases and discomfort to animals.
2. Pests and diseases of rice crops.	2. Shortage of labor to plant forages.
3. Difficult land preparation during periods of heavy rainfall.	3. Shortage of bulls and male goats.
4. Shortage of labor, especially during land preparation.	4. Artificial insemination unsuccessful.
	5. Scabies and bloat in goats.

their animals at night. However, they did not see this as a problem nor relate it to the stated problem of labor shortage. Although men often cut forages, all family members helped as required. Farmers shared their experiences on how to cope with their animals' problems with flies, mosquitoes, scabies, and bloat. Farmers related artificial insemination (AI) problems more to organizational problems than to animal nutrition. The AI problem and the shortage of breeding bulls were referred to the Livestock Services officers.

The PD was made difficult by the farmers' perception that the Government would help with purchasing additional livestock if they planted forages, because this had been a requirement during the ADB II project for farmers wanting to obtain cattle. At that time, recipients planted king grass (*Pennisetum* hybrid) and many of these plantings failed because of relatively poor soils and long dry seasons.

The discussion then focused on how to control *I. cylindrica*. Farmers offered several potential solutions: full cultivation, using herbicides, and planting cover crops. The livestock services officer added, and farmers confirmed, that *Imperata* is often shaded out under trees such as

G. sepium. Farmers were particularly interested in herbicides to control *Imperata*.

At the end of the PD, farmers requested more time to discuss among themselves whether they would continue to work with the FSP. They informed the livestock officer later that the "Maju" farmer group wanted to test the effectiveness of herbicides and cover crops as a group activity. The members of the "Sidodadi" farmer group, who had been relatively passive during the PD, requested planting material of all forages (including grasses) for planting as a group evaluation in a communal area.

Farmer testing of cover crops. After the PD, seed of *C. pubescens* CIAT 15160 (also known as "Centro"), *C. acutifolium* CIAT 5277, and *S. guianensis* CIAT 184 were supplied to the "Maju" group for testing as cover crops. The group was given funds to purchase the herbicide they requested and a knapsack sprayer. The leader of the farmer group initially carried out testing with help from the other group members. Instead of planting the legumes as cover crops into *I. cylindrica* or as fallow improvement after crops, he planted them as intercrops with cassava or maize, sown concurrently with the crop into a fully prepared seedbed. The leader also tested the effectiveness of the herbicide. The farmer group eventually selected intercropping for growing Centro.

Farmer testing of forages has been informal. Apart from the initial nursery plots, farmers decided where and how to plant the species they wanted to evaluate. In fact, during the PD and planning, discussion centered on using legumes as cover crops during crop fallows, not as companion crops. Allowing farmers to decide for themselves has resulted in a forage technology that researchers did not foresee. Nonetheless, researchers influenced the selection of species to test as cover crops.

Seed and planting material of forages were made available to the "Sidodadi" group for planting in a communal area. Farmers chose the species to be included from the "Maju's" nursery area.

1997

More farmers began to expand the area of forages on their own land. Farmers of both the "Maju" and "Sidodadi" groups showed strong interest in evaluating Centro for fallow improvement, because they had heard (and seen) from the "Maju" group leader that this species was effective in suppressing *I. cylindrica*. Many farmers also planted cut-and-carry grasses for supplementary animal feeding.

In early 1997, farmers requested seed of Centro for testing on their own land. Because seed of the selected accession *C. pubescens* CIAT 15160 was unavailable, farmers received seed of common Centro (a different accession). Farmers planted it but quickly complained that it was less vigorous and effective in suppressing weeds than the accession CIAT 15160, which

they had already observed. Seed of CIAT 15160 became available in July 1997 and was distributed to farmers. Many farmers have cultivated areas with the intention of planting Centro at the start of the rainy season in late 1997.

Some farmers started to expand their areas of grasses for cut-and-carry feed in 1997. According to these farmers, a main advantage of planting forages is the quick and easy access to feed for their animals, especially when they do not have time to cut naturally occurring forages and also to supplement other feed resources. This links back to the lack of labor available on farms identified during the PD as a major constraint. Many farmers of both groups intend to plant larger areas of cut-and-carry grasses.

The researchers felt that farmers were not making the most of the nitrogen fixation feature of the legume and discussed this issue with the farmer group. On researchers' advice, the farmers agreed to conduct a group experiment to observe how growing cover crop legumes affected the subsequent yield of maize. They are conducting this experiment on the same plots on which the original forage species evaluation had been conducted.

Outcomes of the Farmer Participatory Research

Assessing technical results in Makroman is difficult at this early stage. Clearly, early results with the cover crop *C. pubescens* CIAT 15160 encouraged farmers. They are developing a technology that researchers did not "recommend". The leader of the "Maju" group claims that growing this cover crop in association with maize and cassava greatly reduces weeding requirements and that crop yields are as high as or higher than those from monoculture. Many farmers have started to test this technology on their own farms and results will be available in 1998.

Farmers growing intensively managed grasses for supplementary feeding reported labor savings as the most important reason for planting forages. Open-ended evaluation and preference ranking were used to capture farmers' experiences with different species. Important criteria for selection of forages by farmers include palatability, ease of cutting (i.e., upright growth habit, less itchiness during cutting, fewer injuries or cuts to hands by sharp leaves), high productivity, and nutritive value (good animal growth).

Farmers most often preferred the grass *Paspalum atratum* BRA 0910. Most farmers, however, prefer mixing different species (both to grow in the field and to feed the animals) to monocrops. These early results are likely to change as farmers gain more experience with these species.

Both the above examples have yielded results that conventional research could not have obtained.

Toward Farmer Participation: Lessons Learned from Makroman

The FSP's experiences in implementing FPR methods at sites like Makroman taught us many lessons, both about the methodologies and about our understanding of farmers' needs in relation to forages. Many potential pitfalls lie in using FPR, but also many benefits, if the methods are implemented with commitment.

In the past 20 years, forage research and development has expanded considerably in Southeast Asia. In several countries, adapted species have been identified from on-station research and substantial quantities of forage seed are now being produced in Thailand and southern China (Phaikaew et al., 1997). Despite these efforts, farmer adoption of forages has been disappointing.

We argue that forages cannot be promoted in isolation from the way they are grown and used on farms. We define forage technologies as the way forages can be grown and used within farming systems. An example of a successful forage technology is the tree legume *G. sepium* grown as fence lines in Bali. Farmers use this tree legume to control animals (or protect crops from stray animals); the leaves are used to supplement dry season feed. Farmers consider the advantages and disadvantages of the forage technology as a whole, not just the advantages and disadvantages of the species.

Although we identified several forage species that are well adapted to the environment, we clearly lacked a good understanding of how these can be grown and used in resource-poor farming systems.

Farmer participatory research methods have given partners in the FSP the approach they have long needed to work with smallholders in developing agricultural technologies. None of the people involved in the FSP (neither staff nor partners) had any background in FPR before attending a workshop in August 1995. Through this workshop and subsequent in-country courses, most participants became aware of the inadequacy of the "top-down" approach commonly used by development workers. Important factors contributing to this change included:

1. Analyzing the role of farmers and development workers in "top-down" and FPR approaches;

2. Becoming aware of the limitation of our communication skills through exercises, role play, and interacting with farmers; and

3. Practicing PD and participatory evaluation (PE) with farmers, leading to the realization that farmers are knowledgeable about their farming systems, that they are able to analyze problem-cause relationships with ease, and that many have already tried to solve their problems in innovative ways.

Not all researchers and development workers sympathize with the FPR approach, however. We learned that development workers (who have years of experience in telling farmers what to do) cannot be made into enthusiastic advocates of FPR overnight. Training courses in FPR can build the skills of those who already sympathize with the concept of empowering farmers. Others will become sensitized to the methods but will not be inclined to use them when they return to their usual work environment. For those in agreement with the approach, their confidence and skills must be strengthened by following up with on-site experience and by providing backup.

Careful Site Selection Is Essential

The term "site selection" refers to both choosing the area in which to work and choosing farmers in that area with whom to work. Both are crucial for successful technology development.

In the case study, Makroman was selected according to secondary information (data, visits to the area, and discussion with key government officials and farmers). Also according to secondary information, development workers had concluded that farmers

had a serious problem with animal feed shortages. As discovered during the PD, however, farmers did not feel that they had a problem with forages but were more concerned about the difficulties of controlling *I. cylindrica*. The PD diagnosis provided the development workers with a clearer understanding of the needs and motivations of the participating farmers than did secondary information. Once the FSP started working with farmers on "their" problems (instead of problems as perceived by outsiders), farmers rapidly became more interested in participating in technology development and evaluation.

The experience in Makroman— that farmers are interested in planting forages only to become eligible for credit from rural banks or government for buying animals—is common throughout the region. Livestock promotion programs exist in most countries and distributing animals to "good" farmers (often defined as those who will plant forages before receiving livestock) is commonly practiced by agricultural agencies. This had occurred recently in Makroman, where the Livestock Services started a goat dispersal project primarily rewarding farmers for participating in the FSP. Although increasing animal numbers and forage development can go hand in hand, distribution programs have complicated our work because farmers' true motivations for planting forages is difficult to assess. We are frequently facing the question: "Do the farmers really have a problem feeding their animals, or are they trying to become recipients in livestock distribution schemes?"

From our experiences at Makroman and other sites, the FSP has developed the following issues to consider in site selection:

1. Are farmers facing a serious problem that can be addressed by introducing forage technologies, and are many farmers affected?

2. Do many farmers perceive the problem as being serious and are they looking for ways to overcome it?

3. Are farmers interested in the project and willing to work with it?

4. Are our national partners able to support work at these sites?

5. Are local development workers (and support from their office) available to join the project?

6. Do effective farmer groups exist, and would they constitute an advantage in a given situation?

Table 3 presents a framework and the minimum information required for site selection and characterization.

Problem Diagnosis: A Powerful Tool

Participatory problem diagnosis has provided us with the means for defining farmers' needs. In Makroman, it helped redirect the emphasis of research from forages for livestock feed to legume cover crops for weed control and soil improvement. It is a powerful tool.

In Makroman, as at many other FSP sites, the PD was complicated by farmers' expectation that the government may provide help with the purchase of additional animals. Obviously, farmers were disappointed when advised that a livestock dispersal project was not to take place and they almost decided not to continue with forages. Farmers only started to become excited about the benefits of forages when the cover crop experiment

showed clear benefits in terms of reduced labor requirements for weeding upland crops. In the case of Makroman, the PD clearly helped the FSP to focus on the needs of farmers (i.e., reducing labor requirements by controlling *I. cylindrica*).

At other sites, farmers have frequently produced more complete, problem-cause diagrams during the PD than did the farmers at Makroman. Figure 2 presents an example of such a problem-cause relationship, as analyzed by farmers during a participatory diagnosis on problems related to raising livestock in Matalom Village, Leyte, Philippines (Gabunada et al. 1997).

Ideally, the PD should be conducted without bias toward particular technologies. Obviously, this is a complication for a project such as the FSP, which is clearly identified with forages ("Hi, I am from the Forages project – what are your problems?"). We have to be aware of these complications, which, usually, can be addressed during the PD. The Makroman case clearly shows that verifying PD results and regularly reassessing farmers' problems and needs are important.

Frequently, as in Makroman, our partners are also responsible in their government positions for livestock distribution and promotion. This has led to farmers being confused and entertaining false expectations. We need to recognize that our local partners have many bosses. Their professional worth is often measured in ways that are difficult to reconcile with FPR methods (such as promotion of particular technologies, number of technology packages distributed). Nonetheless, the success of any project depends on having an enthusiastic development worker in the area and the FSP is always looking for ways of rewarding and supporting such people.

Table 3.   The minimum information needed for site selection for farmer participatory research (FPR).

Required data	Information source[a]
Information for an on-farm site[b]	
Location (e.g., latitude, nearest towns, road access)	d
General description (e.g., human population, history of settlement, sources of income)	d, i
Landscape (topography, altitude range, vegetation)	d, i
Land-use systems	d, i
Long-term climate data (at least 10 years) for:	
Monthly rainfall and number of rain days per month	d
Mean and extreme monthly maximum and minimum temperatures	d
Incidence of catastrophes such as typhoons and flooding	d, i
Soils:	
pH, texture, and drainage	d, i
Broad fertility status, known fertility deficiencies	d, i
Information for an FPR site[c]	
Brief description of area, focusing on key issues affecting development	i, PD
Description of topography, soils, and local climate if different from general area	d, i, PD
Land-use systems:	
Relative land area for each use (%)	i, PD
Topographic location of each land use	PD
Main land-use systems and their benefits or constraints	PD
Inputs used in agriculture	PD
How uncropped land is used	PD
Land ownership system	PD
Livestock farming systems:	
Types, number, and distribution	d, i, PD
Why livestock are kept (e.g., production systems)	PD
Proportion of farmers keeping livestock	d, i, PD
Ownership (e.g., is shared ownership of livestock common?)	PD
Inputs used in raising livestock (e.g., supplementary feeding, veterinary services, chemicals)	PD
Livestock management (e.g., feeding systems: are animals grazed all year or fed cut feed? Who in family is involved and how?)	PD
Livestock marketing	PD
Main constraints and opportunities	PD
Farmers' methods of dealing with these to date	PD
How farmers want to deal with these in future	PD
Trends in the farming system:	
Changes happening within farming system	PD
Changes happening within livestock-raising system	PD
Main sources of income of farm families	i, PD
Other rural development programs that have been or are currently working in this area	i, PD

a. d = data and maps; i = key information and observations; PD = participatory diagnosis.
b. Brief description of the farming systems and physical features of the area surrounding the on-farm site (district or province level).
c. Description of the farming systems at the FPR site (including all farmers at the site, whether with or without livestock).

A further complication has resulted because the FSP is only a single-commodity project—we offer only forage technologies. Farmers, however, usually identify a range of problems during a PD that cannot be addressed with forage technologies. This can disappoint farmers. An approach to minimizing this problem is, wherever possible, to link with broad-based government and nongovernment rural development programs that have, through their own PD approaches, identified many problems important to farmers, some of which the FSP can address. The FSP is currently working

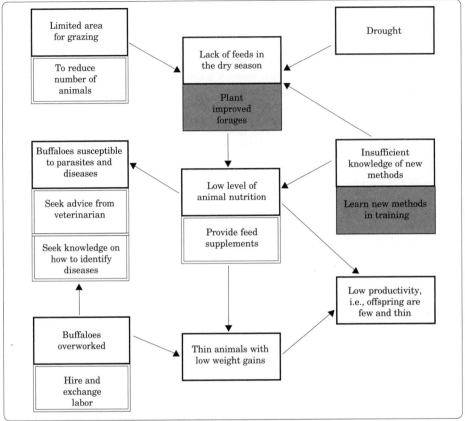

Figure 2. Problem diagnosis of feed resources by smallholders in Matalom Village, Leyte, Philippines. (After Gabunada et al. 1997.) (□ = problems; ▢ = farmers' response; ▣ = possible future solutions.)

with more than 15 such development programs.

Lastly, we can only commit ourselves to working with farmers if we are confident that we have forages available that are likely to help solve the identified problem. Any solution has to be clearly superior to what farmers have available already.

Planning and working with farmers need speed and commitment

We have found that farmers want quick action after a PD. Often they have had previous contact with government and nongovernment agencies and have learnt that much talk and little action is usual. For farmers to realize that the development worker is committed, our aim must always be to move beyond simply conducting PDs and to immediately take up participatory planning and testing of potential technologies. In several cases, farmers expressed surprise that the FSP returned, and delivered what they had promised during the PD and planning sessions.

At Makroman and other sites, the FSP helps farmers and development workers evaluate forages in a variety of ways, from informal testing to more controlled experiments. The type of evaluation depends on what farmers and development workers want. At most sites, farmer testing has been conducted informally with farmers deciding which species to try, where and how to plant, and how to use the forages.

A difficult issue for the FSP has been giving farmers information without telling them what to do. Often farmers do not want detailed information but are keen to get planting material and to experience growing the forages themselves. Farmers plant the same species in different ways depending on their previous experiences and needs. Allowing farmers to experiment with the species and find their own solutions is an important component of the FSP. However, input from researchers into planning and during farmer evaluation is also important. Valuable contributions can be made with technical information on species and technologies based on experiences from other researchers and farmers, adding a more global perspective to local problems.

Often an influential farmer will determine which species farmers will test on their own farms, such as occurred in Makroman with the leader of the "Maju" group. He had the most experience with forages and shared his experiences freely with the other farmers. This situation is common at many FSP sites. Having a champion farmer, who is respected in the community and is keen to try new technologies, has been beneficial. These farmers evaluate by themselves and, if they see opportunities for new technologies, become champions of those new technologies.

Sometimes planning has been difficult. Farmers are unfamiliar with the range of forages available or the way they can be grown and used. Field days in which farmers visit forage nurseries have been useful but, more often, farmers want to grow and experience forages themselves or as a group. At many FSP sites, the initial agreement has been to plant a communal nursery for familiarization and as a source of planting material. Farmers obtained planting material of species they liked from these nurseries for planting on their own land. The FSP tried to give farmers as much information as they wanted on the different species, their feeding value, ways to grow them, and so forth, on field days and other training opportunities.

Giving out seed and planting material to many farmers has had variable results. Although some farmers had great success, others failed with the same seed. From this experience we learned that:

1. Success is not determined by the quantity of seed distributed, but by farmers' motivation to solve their own problems and the capacity of the technology to achieve this.

2. Working with a few enthusiastic farmers who champion a technology results in its more rapid adoption and spread than trying to work with many farmers from the start.

3. Farmers need support and information in evaluating forages on their own land. Regular visits and informal "farmer training" are crucial for success. Working with farmers in this way takes time and commitment. Not a "quick-fix" solution, it requires long-term commitment from all involved.

Evaluating outcomes with farmers needs to be flexible

The FSP continues experimenting with different ways of capturing farmers' experiences. Although FPR methods such as open-ended evaluation and preference ranking are useful tools, they are insufficient in themselves and need to be modified to suit particular situations. Simple, open-ended, and probing questioning often results in a good understanding of farmers' reasons, but these are difficult to quantify and compare across farms. A major outcome of farmer evaluations is a better understanding of the way farmers grow and use forages (i.e., develop forage technologies). Better ways of capturing and quantifying farmer experiences are needed.

Some general results are emerging from across-site comparisons: farmers in upland areas share similar problems (Table 4); they are also interested in intensively managed, backyard forage plots (Table 5).

Table 4.   Major constraints identified by farmer groups in participatory diagnosis at Forages for Smallholders (FSP) sites in upland areas of Southeast Asia.

Major constraints	Number of sites
Feed shortage in dry season (mainly quality)	12
General feed shortage (quantity and quality)	8
Weed invasion (e.g., *Imperata*, *Cromolaena*)	7
Declining soil fertility	3
Lack of control of livestock (e.g., crop damage)	3
Labor shortage (overall or seasonal)	2
Soil erosion	2

Table 5.   Forage technologies evaluated by farmer groups at Forages for Smallholders (FSP) sites in upland areas of Southeast Asia.

Forage technologies evaluated by farmers	Number of sites
Intensively managed plots for cut-and-carry forage	14
Protein banks	6
Contour hedgerows	5
Legumes in crop fallows or grown in association with crops	5
Grasses and legumes for grazing	5
Tree legumes in fence lines	3
Cover crops	3

Conclusions

Marie Antoinette, the wife of Louis XIV of France, when told that the peasants were starving is said to have replied, "Let them eat cake". By her reply she demonstrated how removed from the needs and realities of the common people the French aristocracy had become ... and for this the aristocrats lost their heads in the revolution of 1789.

Fortunately, the consequences of ignoring farmers' perceptions and needs are not as serious for us as they were for Marie Antoinette. However, if we want to improve livelihoods of resource-poor farmers the message is the same:

Ignore farmers' needs and perceptions at your peril!

References

Gabunada Jr, FG; Stür WW; Horne PM. 1997. Development of forage components through farmer participatory research. Proc. XVIII International Grassland Congress, June 8-19, held in Winnipeg (Manitoba) and Saskatoon (Saskatchewan), Canada. Session 24, p 33-34.

Phaikaew C; Guodao L; Abdullah A; Tuhulele M; Magboo E; Bouahom B; Stür WW. 1997. Tropical forage seed production in Southeast Asia: current status and prospects. Proc. XVIII International Grassland Congress, June 8-19, held in Winnipeg (Manitoba) and Saskatoon (Saskatchewan), Canada. Session 28, p 7-8.

CHAPTER 10

Farmers' Independent Experimentation with Green Manure and/or Cover Crops: A Component of Participatory Research for Improving Ugandan Farming Systems

C. S. Wortmann*, C. K. Kaizzi**, and M. Fischler***

Introduction

Participatory research (PR) in this paper refers to farmer-researcher interactions of collaborative and collegiate types (Biggs 1989) with consultative and, even in one case, contractual research occurring concurrently. The research with the Ikulwe community in Uganda evolved from earlier on-farm research for verifying varieties and adapting soil management practices. The community-based, participatory approach to systems improvement was adopted primarily to make formal agricultural research for the agroecological zone more effective. Thus, a continuous, long-term working relationship of researchers with farmers was needed for a fuller integration of farmers in the research process.

Through PR in the Ikulwe area we sought to generate information and technical prototypes of relevance to farmers throughout the larger agroecological zone of which the Ikulwe area is representative. The PR offered "a 'menu' of potentially useful options to be screened, and perhaps modified, by the end-users themselves" (Ashby and Sperling 1995).

Additional "spin-off" benefits were anticipated. These included developing researcher skills and methods in working with farmers (Walker and Wortmann 1994), and improving farmers' problem-solving abilities. The latter could be achieved by giving farmers access to information and additional research skills, and their having an interactive, problem-solving relationship with researchers. Also anticipated were lessons leaent on integrating participatory approaches into the national agricultural research system and how farmers might be more effective as forces in demand-driven research (Merrill-Sands and Collion 1993). These potential outputs were not addressed systematically; but valuable information was obtained (Fischler et al. 1997; Wortmann and Sengooba 1995).

The Ikulwe community consists of five villages (Mayuge, Buyemba, Mugeri, Kavule, and Igamba), whose farmers belong to the the Ikulwe District Farmers' Institute. The Ikulwe area was judged to be representative of most parts of other districts: Iganga,

*   CIAT, Kampala, Uganda.
**   Kawanda Agricultural Research Institute, Kampala, Uganda.
*** Programa de Agricultura Sostenible de Laderas en Centro América (PASOLAC) of the Instituto Interamericano de Cooperación para la Agricultura (IICA), San Salvador, El Salvador.

Kamuli, Jinja, and Mukono. The farming system is typically traditional, based on banana and coffee. Spatial and temporal crop and agronomic diversity is high, with six prominent crops produced in varied associations, plus numerous lesser crops and livestock species (Wortmann and Kaizzi 1997). The terrain comprises rolling hills with wide valleys. The two rainy seasons have similar rainfall, and temperature varies little throughout the year. Farm size averages 1.8 ha, with 70% of the land being used during a typical season for food or cash crop production. The soil is usually low in P. Farmers purchase few agricultural inputs and do not traditionally use fertilizers, which are not readily available.

Participatory Research in the Ikulwe Area

Participatory research was initiated in 1992, when farmers collaborated with researchers during a 4-day, participatory, rural appraisal. This preliminary effort aimed to characterize farming systems, and identify and diagnose problems. In 1993, researchers from the Ugandan National Agricultural Research Organization (NARO) and CIAT, and a government extension agent again worked with farmers to further characterize and diagnose, and prioritize problems and research opportunities, and develop a research plan with farmers. The plan was regularly revised at semi-annual meetings intended to evaluate results obtained, and to plan for the following season.

The PR was kept closely linked with on-station and other on-farm research activities, and addressed some unique topics. The types of researcher-farmer interactions varied with research activities: some were planned and designed by researchers alone, others by farmers and researchers jointly, and yet others by farmers alone (farmers' independent experimentation [FIE]). In nearly all cases, farmers who participated in the evaluation managed the trials. Participation was first consultative and collaborative (Bentley 1994; Biggs 1989), but evolved to be more collegial as FIE increased.

The cost effectiveness of PR has been of concern. A major expense comprises researcher visits to the community (e.g., vehicle operation, overnight allowances, researcher's time). Maintaining an effective balance between costs and researcher time with the community was a struggle. We estimate that the mean time spent actually working in the community has been 2-3 researcher-days per month. Use of community-based facilitators has contributed greatly to minimizing costs and improving the timeliness of implementation. At first, a farmer and an extension worker were facilitators; now two farmers serve part-time as field research assistants. They help establish the more difficult trials, collect and compile data, and assist in surveys as interpreters and/or enumerators. They were, at first, paid monthly, but now on a fee-for-task basis.

Farmer participation was voluntary; farmers were not selected, and women were encouraged to participate. The PR maintained a strong and active core of about eight farmers who typically have two or more formal trials per season and experiment independently. Another 12 farmers have continued to participate less actively, and another 10 to 20 farmers come and go, typically staying active for only 1 to 3 seasons.

Responsibilities and roles were normally allocated at semi-annual meetings, but often incompletely because of time factors. Community-based facilitators then identified farmers for these activities.

The need for a PR committee to govern and guide the work was much discussed for several years (Wortmann and Walker 1994), but only implemented in 1996. Participating farmers decided that the committee should be composed solely of farmers: three men and three women. Delegated responsibilities of the committee included supervising and guiding the PR in Ikulwe, encouraging farmers to participate, identifying needs and opportunities to be addressed, liaising with research, and organizing meetings. The committee has not performed well; but recently received encouragement in the form of about US$300 per year for expenses, communications, and purchase of supplies and equipment for research activities. Accountability for use of the funds is required.

The PR in Ikulwe has generated much information on numerous technical alternatives. The process has been well documented: researchers eventually compiled information into various reports and extension materials (Wortmann et al. 1998). Crop variety evaluations resulted in at least some adoption of six bean, one upland rice, and two cassava varieties. Preliminary results indicate possibly two promising sweetpotato varieties. Integrated pest management components were verified for banana weevil and mole rat control, with good adoption of the latter. Research on soil fertility management resulted in many options for use of green manure and cover crops (GMCCs), of organic materials with small quantities of fertilizers, living barriers for erosion control, and N_2 fixation.

Indicators of achievement were not determined in advance for secondary benefits of PR, and certain aspects of PR were not monitored or evaluated. Any comment on successes and failures of the PR in Ikulwe must therefore be qualitative and subjective.

Positive points were:

1. The PR has been continuous over eight seasons.

2. The approach apparently stimulated the effective FIE that occurred.

3. Farmers are more capable in implementing trials, and site-level operational costs are low relative to the value of information gained.

4. Farmers may be more capable in obtaining information (supplementary to their own or as new ideas) and applying it to solve problems or capitalize on opportunities.

Although the NARO now recognizes the value of involving farmers in research, we cannot assess the influence that the PR in Ikulwe had in bringing this about.

Negative points were:

1. The FPR committee was formed late and did not function well.

2. Only eight farmers were highly active, while another 40 participated on a less frequent basis.

3. No community problems were addressed, such as the availability of inputs, management of common resources, or conflicts over access to resources.

4. The intent that characterization and diagnosis be an on-going process was not well pursued and, although researchers continued to gain an improved understanding of

the farmers' situation, the information was not well documented.

5. Problems related to postharvest handling, marketing, and livestock were not addressed.

6. NARO's institutional commitment to the work was weak.

Evaluation of Farmers' Independent Experimentation

Distinguishing between FIE and adoption

An exciting aspect of the PR in Ikulwe has been the FIE, which greatly improved the cost-effectiveness of PR.

We conducted a session with farmers in 1993 to learn of their attempts to test new alternatives and their methods of field-testing and evaluation. The farmers could only cite one or two cases of having brought a new variety from another location. The researchers learned little of farmers' current FIE practices through this exercise. Possibly, a language problem was to blame or the farmers' perception of experimentation differed from that of the researchers. During subsequent farm visits, we observed cases of farmers trying alternatives, and undoubtedly many cases of FIE were overlooked in these agronomically diverse systems. Although not well documented, these observations did verify that FIE was occurring.

When is it really experimentation and when is it adoption? In many cases, farmers accept a technical alternative as appropriate, but with some doubt or expectation that it may need adaptation for their situations. In these cases, they practice FIE in that

they usually experiment within a small area, effectively leaving the rest of the field as a control, and often make some modifications. Collaborative activities during the PR in Ikulwe apparently stimulated much FIE. Several elements of PR may have contributed:

1. Farmers recognized that they were part of a collaborative research process;

2. Farmers obtained new information on how they might integrate technical alternatives into their farming systems;

3. Farmers obtained an initial supply of planting material; and

4. Farmers interacted with other PR farmers who encouraged them and shared ideas.

Farmers used FIE several technical options, but primarily to find different ways of integrating GMCC species into their cropping systems. The FIE methods varied. Leaving a control plot was uncommon, and sometimes a whole field was sown to the GMCC (e.g., intercropping *Crotalaria* under coffee or *Canavalia* under banana). Treatments were seldom replicated; and yields were usually not measured. Using small-to-moderate test plots was common but only a few farmers measured the plots to ensure that these were of similar size.

Obtaining information from FIE on GMCCs

Although researchers recognized the potential for obtaining valuable information from FIE on GMCCs, we could not respond immediately because of other commitments and lack of experience with appropriate methods. Eventually, we and the farmers used four methods to gain information from the FIE on GMCCs:

Method I. Researchers and a group of interested farmers visited the FIE sites during the growing season to observe and discuss the results with implementing farmers. This approach probably yielded the best information on agronomic aspects such as interactions of GMCCs with associated and subsequent crops, and with weeds, effects on soil, and labor and skill requirements. Different people collected data, albeit not systematically: visits were at different times and reflected different interests. Information was usually badly recorded and analyzed. Much of it came from researchers' memories when the information was finally applied in developing a decision-making guide for using GMCCs.

Method II. Farmers who had experimented with GMCCs met in small groups to list the main benefits and problems associated with each species (Fischler 1997). Although farmers and a researcher identified major points of discussion beforehand, these may have reflected more the criteria of the researcher than of the farmers (assuming significant differences). Discussions addressed

opportunities and problems with GMCCs, benefits to the soil and to subsequent crops, weed suppression, and labor requirements. Information and opinions were openly exchanged; and the enthusiasm of a few farmers for particular GMCC practices tended to sway discussions. Farmers enjoyed the exercise, which took little time. The well-recorded results were descriptive and qualitative (Fischler 1997; Fischler and Wortmann 1997).

Method III. Twelve farmers individually assessed four GMCC species for eight criteria, using a counter method of matrix ranking. This allowed individuals to express their preferences and discuss the relative importance of each criterion. The exercise required a moderate amount of researchers' time, although, again, the farmers enjoyed it. The method allowed farmers' preferences to be quantitatively assessed with estimates of means and variances (Table 1). Some individuals lacked experience with one or more of the GMCC species-criteria combinations; some declined to make an estimate; and others attempted an estimate based on what little they knew, which

Table 1. Evaluation of four green manure species by 12 farmers, using a matrix ranking method, for different production methods and uses[a], Uganda.

Green manure species	Evaluated as, or for:							
	Sole crop	Intercropped with:				Fodder quality	Soil improve-ment	Weed suppression
		Banana	Maize	Sweetpotato	Cassava			
Crotalaria	5.7	4.4	5.0	4.3	4.8	2.5	6.4	5.4
Canavalia	4.7	6.8	4.2	3.8	5.0	0.9	5.5	6.0
Mucuna	8.8	6.3	6.0	0.6	6.8	5.2	8.7	9.0
Lablab	8.1	5.3	4.7	0.8	5.0	7.5	7.7	7.9
LSD (P = 0.05)	1.04	1.77	1.26	2.03	ns	2.09	1.06	1.27
MSv[b]	32	30	31	17	36	23	32	32

a. On a scale of 1 to 9, where 1 = unfavorable and 9 = favorable.
b. Degrees of freedom for the mean square.
SOURCE: Fischler and Wortmann 1997.

probably resulted in larger variances. The evaluation was according to criteria set by researchers after consulting a few experienced farmers. The reasons for farmers' preference rankings were less well captured than they might have been.

Method IV. Nineteen farmers were interviewed, using an open-ended, probing approach on 49 experiments (35 FIE and 14 formal) where they had used a GMCC species. Most farmers had more than one case to consider. *Canavalia, Crotalaria, Lablab,* and *Mucuna* were considered, and these were grown as sole crops and in a wide variety of intercrops (Table 2), including with maize, bean, banana, coffee, cassava, or sweetpotato. The information gained was based on farmers' personal experiences with the GMCCs. Information that directly reflected farmers' actual practice, for example, the frequency of planting GMCCs under different conditions, allowed for sound assessments. Other information reflected their perceptions. The approach invited farmers to freely express opinions and criticisms with the expectation that the evaluation of benefits, problems, and opportunities was according to farmers' criteria (Tables 3 and 4). Probing, on the other hand, was expected to result in researcher influence on the information obtained.

The four methods yielded similar information but with differences in type and quality. Some differences occurred because the information sought was not fully consistent across the four methods.

Preference did not always accurately reflect practice. Method III showed only slightly more preference for intercropping *Canavalia* with banana, but method IV found *Canavalia*-banana intercropping to be far more common than other *Canavalia* production practices. Method III indicated that *Mucuna* was best suited to sole-crop production, and of similar suitability for several intercrop associations; but method IV found that intercropping *Mucuna* with maize was far more common than any other *Mucuna* production practice. The latter discrepancy is not unexpected: although the preference may be for sole-crop production of *Mucuna*, land scarcity restricts its use.

The method IV criteria and their prioritization (Table 2) are similar to those indirectly indicated by

Table 2. Preferences for sole crop and intercrop production of green manure and/or cover crop species as indicated by the percentage of farmers interviewed who had used the practice, Uganda.

Crop	Green manure and/or cover crop[a]			
	Canavalia (n = 11)	*Mucuna* (n = 17)	*Lablab* (n = 11)	*Crotalaria* (n =10)
Banana	73 (73)	18 (18)	18 (18)	10 (10)
Coffee	0	0	9 (9)	10 (10)
Banana/coffee	18 (18)	0	0	0
Maize	9 (9)	88 (53)	73 (18)	90 (20)
Sweetpotato	9 (9)	0	0	0
Bean	0	0	0	80 (10)
Cassava	0	18 (18)	0	10 (10)
Sole crop	0	6	18	10

a. n = number of farmers.
  Values in parentheses = percentages of farmers who practiced cropping as farmers' independent experimentation rather than part of researcher-farmer designed experimentation.

Table 3. Positive features of four green manure and/or cover crop species as indicated by percentages of farmers mentioning the characteristic, Uganda.

Positive features	Green manure and/or cover crop[a]			
	Canavalia (n = 11)	Mucuna (n = 17)	Lablab (n = 11)	Crotalaria (n = 10)
Improves soil fertility	82	88	91	100
Suppresses weeds	55	47	45	50
Keeps soil cool, reduces evaporation	64	41	27	0
Uprooting easy	18	0	0	0
Produces much seed	18	29	0	30
Prolonged growth	9	0	18	0
Good fodder	0	12	64	0
Reduces erosion	27	29	18	30
Improves soil tilth	0	4	0	0

a. n = number of farmers.

Table 4. Undesirable features of four green manure and/or cover crop species as indicated by the percentages of farmers mentioning the fault, Uganda.

Undesirable features	Green manure and/or cover crop[a]			
	Canavalia (n = 11)	Mucuna (n = 17)	Lablab (n = 11)	Crotalaria (n = 10)
Climbs on associated crops	0	76	45	0
Seeds are inedible	18	18	0	0
Laborious to produce	0	12	0	70
Difficult to uproot	0	18	7	10
Difficult to thresh	0	6	0	30

a. n = number of farmers.

method III, and to those of researchers. Effect on soil fertility was most mentioned. Suppression of weeds, labor requirement, and climbing on associated crops were often mentioned. Fodder quality, effect on soil erosion, and effect on soil moisture were less frequently cited. The presence of researchers may have affected the responses of farmers, that is, they may have replied with preconceived ideas of what the researchers wanted to hear. The exercises did not reveal any criteria that farmers had not considered. Researchers' criteria were often expressed during earlier interactions with farmers and these may have influenced those used by farmers.

Adoption and Dissemination of GMCC Practices

Although some loose collaboration had been initiated with nongovernment organizations (NGOs) earlier, researchers began working with farmers to disseminate information from the PR in Ikulwe in 1996. The information disseminated concerns a wide range of technical options, with the GMCC alternatives being prominent. Activities included:

1. Preparing printed material consisting of a decision guide to the use of four GMCC species (Table 5) and specific information for each of the species;

2. Groups of farmers visiting Ikulwe PR sites (often facilitated by NGOs) to observe and discuss practices adopted by participating farmers;

3. Participating farmers and researchers attending agricultural shows to inform inquiring farmers; and

4. Preparing a local group to use drama for sensitization on relevant issues and to disseminate information (this activity has been delayed because of other commitments of the professional drama group, which is now assisting with script development and training).

Although no efforts were externally supported to specifically promote GMCC technology in Ikulwe, the PR resulted in spontaneous adoption and dissemination. Rate of adoption was assessed in late 1995 by interviewing 22 farmers who had taken part in GMCC research. Farmers who had previously participated in experimenting with a species and had a crop during the current growing season were considered to have adopted. However, it was recognized that some may have been continuing their experiments and some who did not have a species during the season could

Table 5. Guidelines to the use of four green manure species in central and eastern Uganda.

If you want to.....	plant	but not........
Produce a sole crop	*Mucuna* or *Lablab*	*Canavalia*
Intercrop with maize	*Canavalia*, or *Lablab* at minimal planting density	*Mucuna*
Intercrop with newly planted banana or coffee	*Canavalia*	*Mucuna* or *Lablab*
Intercrop with established ban ana or coffee	*Canavalia* or *Mucuna* at low planting density	*Crotalaria*
Intercrop between sweetpotato mounds	*Crotalaria* or *Canavalia*	*Mucuna* or *Lablab*
Intercrop with newly planted cassava	*Canavalia* or *Crotalaria* between rows of cassava	*Mucuna* or *Lablab*
Intercrop with established cassava	*Canavalia* or *Mucuna* at low density	*Crotalaria*
Produce fodder	*Lablab* or *Mucuna*	*Canavalia* or *Crotalaria*
Suppress weeds	*Mucuna* or *Lablab*	*Crotalaria* or *Canavalia*
Reduce nematodes	*Crotalaria*	*Canavalia*
Produce durable mulch	*Crotalaria* and *Canavalia* and allow to mature	*Lablab* or *Mucuna*

SOURCE: Fischler and Wortmann 1997.

plant in another season. Adoption was poor for *Crotalaria* (5%), intermediate for *Mucuna* (43%) and *Lablab* (45%), and high for *Canavalia* (62%). Reasons for discontinuing the use of a species (and number of farmers giving the response) were insufficient labor (17), insufficient land (1), lack of seed (6), no benefit observed (7), and domestic problems such as illness (6). The responses do not apply equally to all species, and insufficient labor was cited frequently for *Crotalaria*. Note that less than 5% mentioned insufficient land as a reason for discontinuing use of a GMCC species, given that land scarcity is often perceived as the major obstacle to GMCC use.

The PR with GMCCs stimulated interest among other farmers who requested seeds from the PR farmers. Most PR farmers reported giving seed of one or more species to several other farmers. Of those who had grown a species previously, 26% did not disseminate seed to other farmers, 27% gave seed to 1-3 others, 26% gave to 4-7, 4% gave to 8-10, 10% gave to 11-18, and 12% gave to more than 20. Adoption by recipient farmers has not been assessed.

Conclusions

The PR in Ikulwe has effectively generated and verified prototypes and information applicable to the mid-altitude farming systems of eastern and central Uganda. A major part of the success has been with GMCCs where four species were well evaluated, using experiments that researchers and farmers, or farmers independently, designed. The PR and FIE processes were badly evaluated, but deserve more study. The FIE has greatly improved the cost effectiveness of the research because much information was gained at little cost. Farmer participatory research should aim to stimulate FIE.

References

Ashby J; Sperling L. 1995. Institutionalizing participatory, client-driven research and technology development in agriculture. Dev Change 26:753-770.

Bentley JW. 1994. Facts, fantasies, and failures of farmer participatory research. Agric Human Values 11:140-150.

Biggs SD. 1989. Resource-poor farmer participation in research: a synthesis of experiences from nine national agricultural research systems. International Service for National Agricultural Research (ISNAR), The Hague, Netherlands. 37 p.

Fischler M. 1997. Legume green manure in the management of maize-bean cropping systems in eastern Africa with special reference to crotalaria (*C. ochroleuca* G. Don.). Ph.D. dissertation. Swiss Federal Institute of Technology, Zürich, Switzerland. 211 p.

Fischler M; Wortmann CS. 1997. Green manure research in eastern Africa—a participatory approach. Paper presented at the International Symposium on the Science and Practice of Short-Term Improved Fallows, 11-15 Mar 1997, Lilongwe, Malawi.

Fischler M; David S; Farley C; Ugen M; Wortmann, C. 1997. Applying farmer participation research methods to planning agricultural research: experiences from eastern Africa. J Farm Syst Res Extens 6:37-54.

Merrill-Sands D; Collion MH. 1993. Making the farmers' voice count in agricultural research. Q J Intern Agric 32:260-272.

Walker FR; Wortmann CS. 1994. Why involve farmers in research? In: Adipala, E; Bekunda MA; Tenywa JS; Ogenga-Latigo MW, eds. Proc. Crop Science Conference for Eastern and Southern Africa, June 1993, Kampala, Uganda. Printed by Makerere University Printery, Kampala, Uganda. p 397-399.

Wortmann CS; Kaizzi CK. 1997. Nutrient balances in eastern and central Uganda. Paper presented at the First All-Africa Crop Science Conference, 14-16 Jan 1997, Pretoria, South Africa.

Wortmann CS; Sengooba T. 1995. Institutionalization of farmer participatory research in Uganda's National Agricultural Research Organization (NARO). Paper presented at a workshop to institutionalize farmer participatory research in NARO, 22-23 May 1995, Kampala, Uganda.

Wortmann CS; Walker FR. 1994. Participatory research—institutional considerations. In: Adipala, E; Bekunda MA; Tenywa JS; Ogenga-Latigo MW, eds. Proc. Crop Science Conference for Eastern and Southern Africa, June 1993, Kampala, Uganda. Printed by Makerere University Printery, Kampala, Uganda. p 400-402.

Wortmann CS; Alifugani F; Fischler M; Kaizzi CK. 1998. Accomplishments of participatory research for systems improvement in Iganga District of eastern Uganda, 1993 to 1997. Network on Bean Research in Africa, Occasional Publications Series no. 27. CIAT, Kampala, Uganda.

CHAPTER 11

Designing Sustainable, Commercial, Farmer Seed Production Systems in Africa: Case Studies from Uganda

Soniia David and *Sarah Kasozi**

Introduction

The formal seed sector in developing countries includes government, private, and commercial seed companies. Such institutions typically produce certified seed in centralized facilities and supply less than 20% of seed of most food crops (Almekinders et al. 1994; Cromwell et al. 1993; Groosman et al. 1991). This figure is even lower for self-pollinating crops such as the common bean (*Phaseolus vulgaris* L.) that bring little profit to seed companies because of uncertain and fluctuating demand caused by competition from farm-saved seed. Only 1%-5% of 360 farm households surveyed in Uganda planted certified bean seed in 1995 (ADC/IDEA 1996). Designing alternative seed production systems must therefore be an urgent priority if this bottleneck in commodity research is to be freed.

This paper reports on CIAT experiences in Uganda with developing one such approach: farmer seed enterprises (FSEs). We propose commercial seed production by farmers as a strategy to sustainably distribute and promote modern crop varieties. "Modern crop varieties" refers to those varieties produced by formal, scientific,

plant breeding methods. Local varieties or landraces, in contrast, are those materials traditionally grown by farmers. Secondary goals of this approach include preserving varietal diversity through multiplying landraces, generating income, and empowering farmers.

The study focused on beans, but most of the principles and guidelines offered can be applied to developing farmer capacity to produce seed of other self-pollinating crops. This study is one of the few attempts by researchers in Africa to support and document farmer-led seed production efforts. It examined the process involved in designing sustainable approaches to seed supply systems on a commercial, but small, scale and the prospects for replicating the approach in a wider regional context.

Some successful efforts in decentralized seed production have been documented in Asia and Latin America, although few involved the common bean (Ashby et al. 1995; Cromwell 1997; Garay et al. nd; Lépiz et al. 1996). Typically, in Africa, local seed production projects involve contract growers and seed exchange schemes (Cromwell et al. 1993; Gaifami 1992) and only a few, such as the Global 2000 project in Ghana, support farmer-led commercial efforts

* Pan-African Bean Research Alliance (PABRA), CIAT, Kampala, Uganda.

(Bockari-Kubei 1994; Hendersen and Singh 1990). Successful approaches have been used in Latin America and Asia. But these may be inappropriate for African conditions, given the poor infrastructure, small markets for agricultural services, often weak national agricultural research systems (NARS), and the absence in some African countries of suitable agencies for implementation such as cooperatives, farmer associations, and nongovernment organizations (NGOs).

No institutional linkages were developed to ensure the sustainability of the seed production activities initiated because we envisaged that the research phase would be followed by pilot projects designed to implement and institutionalize the approach on a wider scale.

Using a case study approach, the present study aimed to assess the feasibility of developing small-scale production units of commercial seed in Africa by addressing the following:

1. Organization:
    What type of farmers can successfully produce bean seed? What scale of production can FSEs achieve? What are farmers' training and funding needs? Is suitable postharvest equipment available, and does it meet producers' needs?

2. Marketing and promotion:
    Does a demand exist for bean seed produced by FSEs, and what is the nature of demand for new varieties? Can FSEs market seed on their own without external assistance? Can FSEs be involved in seed education as a promotional strategy?

3. Seed quality:
    What is the quality of seed produced by FSEs? Which quality standards should be applied to artisanal seed production?

The case studies presented and conclusions reached apply specifically to microenterprises operated by smallholders. Larger enterprises or other types of commercial ventures designed to accelerate varietal dissemination are not discussed.

Initiating Farmer Seed Enterprises

Three farmer groups in eastern Uganda participated in the present study between 1994 and 1996. These were the Ikulwe Bean Farmers' Association (IBFA), which is a mixed group of 10 households in Iganga District; the Makhai Women's Group (MWG) of 10 women, Mbale District; and the Budama Kyelema Turbana Women's Group (BKTWG) of 12 women, also in Mbale District. A fourth group in Mukono District dropped out after completing training in seed production because of internal group problems. By local standards, group members were average or above in terms of resources, skills, educational level, and prior business experience. The BKTWG was the only group that had no previous contacts with external agencies. Unlike the other two groups, which were recruited to participate in seed production, the IBFA initiated seed production on its own in 1993 before the study started. Farmers involved in bean varietal trials formed the group, intending to multiply seed of test varieties. The IBFA had longer involvement in seed production and was composed of both male and female farmers, all of whom had worked closely with researchers in a different participatory research project. This helped make the group distinctive and affected its achievements.

Sociologists undertook the research with technical input from pathologists, entomologists, agricultural engineers, and seed technologists. Two government extension agents regularly monitored the Mbale groups. Members of IBFA chose to discontinue working with the extension agent because of a conflict of interest over his technical role and business interests.

Throughout Uganda, and most of eastern and southern Africa, women's labor contributions to bean production surpasses that of men and they are solely responsible for seed maintenance. In Mbale and Mukono, women's groups were specifically targeted to investigate the feasibility of women's participation in small-scale, commercial seed production. The MWG and BKTWG were selected, after discussions with three other women's groups identified by extension agents. The major criteria used to select the groups were 10 or more members, no or few other group activities, and previous business experience.

Identifying study sites and producers

Level of demand for bean seed was the single most important criterion in selecting study sites. However, factors such as altitude, rainfall, incidence of seed-borne diseases, and other production constraints were recognized as important for successful seed production. In all localities, beans are grown during March-May (season A) and September-November (season B). Production during season B is riskier because of heavy and unpredictable rainfall. Mbale represents an area of high demand for bean seed, with demand being typically lower in Mukono and Iganga Districts. We anticipated that other CIAT research on local bean seed systems and varietal distribution in Mbale and Mukono

Districts would complement the study (David 1996; David et al. 1997).

Training and equipment

Except for IBFA, whose activities predated the study, seed production activities began with a 5-day training workshop. The following topics were covered: disease and pest identification and management, agronomic practices for seed production, postharvest handling of seed, testing of germination and moisture content, market research, marketing and promotion, bookkeeping, costing, and group dynamics. Training workshops were held again in 1997 and additional training offered on an ad hoc basis on disease and pest identification, and management and business skills. Groups were provided with three pieces of equipment: a threshing rack to minimize loss and mechanical damage to the seed, a sorter to facilitate the work and allow for sorting to be done while seated, and black polyethylene sheets for drying. Fields of seed producers were not inspected but seed health testing was conducted over three seasons (incomplete for some groups) to assess pathogen infection levels and germination.

Producers multiplied two cultivars released in 1994: CAL 96 (K 132) and MCM 5001 (K 131). The FSEs did not multiply other varieties released in 1995 because seed was unavailable. Farmers throughout Uganda highly appreciate 'CAL 96', a calima type, because of its close resemblance to the widely grown and highly marketable 'K 20'. On-station yields for 'CAL 96' range between 500 and 1500 kg/ha, that is, 27% more than the yields of 'K 20'. The variety is susceptible to two seed-borne diseases: pythium root rot and common bacterial blight (CBB). 'MCM 5001', a carioca seed type previously unknown in Uganda, is high yielding (1200-2500 kg/ha or 40% more than the yields of 'K 20') but its small size, type II growth habit, and low market demand make it less popular with farmers. This variety is resistant to bean common mosaic virus (BCMV) but susceptible to angular leaf spot (ALS). Although producers were encouraged to multiply seed of local varieties, they showed little interest because of the low productivity of landraces and an anticipated low demand.

Group organization

The three FSEs differed with respect to resources such as education, access to land and labor, prior training, group cohesion, business experience, and mode of organizing production and distributing assets, all of which affected their achievements. For example, the dynamism of the MWG in selling and promoting their seed may be attributed to the higher educational level of its membership, previous training from an NGO in group dynamics and bookkeeping, and stronger group cohesion fostered by that training and the group's longer history. It is probably no coincidence that the BKTWG, a more recently formed group with no prior contact with external agencies, experienced a high drop-out rate and made little effort to market and promote its seed. By 1996, five members had disappointedly left the group because of unmet expectations of financial assistance from CIAT.

Production was organized on either a communal or individual basis. From 1993B to 1994B members of the IBFA planted seed on a communal plot but shifted to individual production in 1995A because motivation was lacking for communal work and land rental costs were high. Individual growers (2-4 each season) were responsible for postharvest tasks. A committee of members conducted inspections of individual fields to check for off-types and diseases. Growers were expected to return all seed produced to the group for storage and marketing and received 25% of the earnings thereof.

Both Mbale groups grew seed on a communal plot (borrowed or rented from neighbors) where all members were required to contribute labor. The Mbale groups hired oxen for land preparation and this delayed planting at least once. Both the MWG and BKTWG sprayed the crop against insect pests, a task the IBFA omitted. No group used fertilizer or other soil improvement measures. All producers tested the germination and moisture content of the seed (using the salt test method) before storage and treated it with Actellic® (pirimiphos-methyl) to control storage pests. Seed was bagged and labeled (in some instances), using locally purchased plastic bags. Because the plastic was weak, bagged quantities weighed either half a kilo or one kilo. In all cases, group members exclusively provided labor for all activities. The IBFA and MWG retained group funds, which, in the latter case, were available as credit to members. The IBFA was the only group to open a bank account.

Mode of operation

A participatory approach was used in training and in all aspects of developing FSEs. The role of researchers was to facilitate the learning process and to support and encourage farmers' decision making, problem solving, and empowerment. Producers made all decisions, including which varieties to multiply. A second element of farmer participation was the focus on farmers' indigenous knowledge of bean diseases and pests. Because their knowledge was limited, farmers were encouraged to coin names for major diseases and pests. To minimize the farmers' taking risks, to stress ownership of the business, and to avoid creating a dependency mentality, equipment and seed were provided on a cost-sharing basis between farmers and CIAT. No form of financial assistance was provided because of the absence of suitable NGO partners who could administer loans.

We visited the groups at least once each season to monitor and plan activities and discuss problems. Extension agents visited the groups more frequently, particularly during field operations, to offer technical advice and collect data. Impact among producers was investigated through an evaluation exercise conducted in 1997 by MWG and BKTWG. An extension officer facilitated the evaluation.

Production and seed quality

Production and productivity by all three enterprises were disappointingly low. The IBFA produced the most seed over seven seasons (2561 kg), followed

by BKTWG (535 kg produced over four seasons), and MWG (478 kg produced over four seasons) (Table 1). Yields per unit area (113-142 kg/ha for 'CAL 96' and 61-100 kg/ha for 'MCM 5001') and multiplication rates (a range of 5-9 for 'CAL 96' and 7-9 for 'MCM 5001') were far less than expected. However, they were similar to mean yields observed among a sample of farmers growing the same varieties in Iganga and Mbale Districts (ADC/IDEA 1996). Despite low yields for both 'CAL 96' (25% of expected yield) and 'MCM 5001' (8%), both cultivars outyielded the widely grown 'K 20': 'CAL 96' by 34% and 'MCM 5001' by 14%.

All producers planted a larger total amount of 'CAL 96' than of 'MCM 5001', reflecting market demand. Despite slow sales of 'MCM 5001', IBFA members continued to plant significant quantities of that variety, surpassing the amount of 'CAL 96' planted in three seasons. Fluctuations from season to season in the amount of seed sown by all groups did not

Table 1. Seed production (kg) by three Bean Farmers' Associations[a], Uganda, 1993-1996.

Quantity of seed type by farmer group	Season							
	1993B	1994A	1994B	1995A	1995B	1996A	1996B	Total
'CAL 96' seed planted								
IBFA	40	50	10	20	82	12	66	280
MWG				15	0	18	22	55
BKTWG				15	10	10	11	46
'MCM 5001' seed planted								
IBFA	10	50	20	69	34	15	10	208
MWG				0.5	9.5	8	0	18
BKTWG				10	0	1.5	0	11.5
Clean seed produced for 'CAL 96'								
IBFA	0	90	50	117	123	105	195	680
MWG				300	0	55	40	395
BKTWG				240	83	40	95	458
Clean seed produced for 'MCM 5001'								
IBFA	0	550	120	536	470	170	35	1881
MWG				10	60	13	0	83
BKTWG				67	0	10	0	77

a. IBFA = Ikulwe Bean Farmers' Association; MWG = Makhai Women's Group; BKTWG = Budama Kyelema Turbana Women's Group.

necessarily reflect anticipated demand but resulted from personal mishaps such as illness. Only the IBFA pursued a strategy of planting larger quantities in season B (1995/96), anticipating higher demand for 'CAL 96' in the following season A.

Economic analysis of production by the two Mbale groups during the first two seasons revealed four important findings (Table 2). First, labor constituted the highest single cost. Second, returns were better during season A because of lower yields in season B, attributed largely to agroclimatic factors. Third, except for MWG in the second season, the cost of seed production by FSEs is lower than on-station production (estimated at 1000 Ugandan shillings per kilogram). Unfortunately, because of lack of data, the study was unable to compare the efficiency of FSEs with contract and nonspecialized farmers. Fourth, judging from output-to-input ratios (excluding season B for MWG), both groups covered their production costs, showing that seed production by farmers is a potentially viable enterprise. However, more discussion is needed to explain the low production by all three groups, and by the Mbale groups after 1995.

Five factors account for the low yields of seed growers:

1. Adverse climatic conditions (drought, hailstorms, and heavy rains);

2. High disease and pest incidence (CBB, ALS, root rots, and various insect pests);

3. Poor cultural practices (poor land preparation, late planting, and wide spacing);

4. Lack of access to resources such as land and oxen; and

5. Poor soils and/or low soil fertility.

Although little can be done about unfavorable climatic conditions, suitable interventions can alleviate the remaining production constraints. High seed loss caused by diseases (a mean range of 13%-37% for 'CAL 96' and 19%-28% for 'MCM 5001') suggests that, in the absence of fungicides, to achieve economic returns, FSEs should limit multiplication to resistant varieties and maintain good crop husbandry. Other suggestions for increasing seed production include hiring labor and purchasing oxen to ease labor bottlenecks, purchasing land specifically for seed production, practicing crop rotation and using fertilizer or other soil improvement amendments (e.g., green manures), and closer supervision of field activities by technical support staff. These options were not explored in the Ugandan case because of the groups' lack of resources, and the absence of financial assistance and full-time technical support staff.

Table 2. Costs of seed production (U Sh[a] per kg) by farmer seed enterprises[b] (FSEs) in Mbale, Uganda, 1995.

Costs	Season A		Season B	
	MWG	BKTWG	MWG	BKTWG
Inputs	58	80	201	138
Labor	211	249	1058	392
Variable costs	269	329	1259	530
Fixed costs[c]	96	111	440	264
Production	365	440	1699	794
Gross margin per unit of bean seed	431	471	-559	271
Output-to-input ratio	1.91	1.82	0.41	1.01

a. U Sh = Ugandan shillings.
b. MWG = Makhai Women's Group; BKTWG = Budama Kyelema Turbana Women's Group.
c. Excludes the cost of land, which was obtained free during both seasons.

Farmers' poor cultural practices also underscored the conflict that smallholders, women in particular, experience between business and household or personal interests. Invariably, the members of the two women's groups attended their household fields before the communal one, resulting in late planting and weeding. Notably, the labor bottlenecks faced by the women's groups were not experienced by the IBFA, whose male members had access to household labor for both food and seed production. This factor, coupled with production on individual plots, explains IBFA's higher production capacity. Because African women usually do not own land, have limited access to household labor, and experience difficulties in preventing male appropriation of their business profits (Wachtel 1976), communal seed growing and group activity appears to work best for them, despite the several drawbacks (e.g., access to land and low motivation to contribute to group work).

The quality of seed produced by the three FSEs surpassed that of seed sold in nearby shops and markets in 1995A in terms of germination rate (a mean of 85%-94% for FSEs, compared with 72%-74% for other commercial sources) and of disease levels. No attempt was made to compare the quality of seed produced by FSEs with seed obtained directly from unspecialized bean farmers. A study conducted in Rwanda observed that, although pathogen infection levels were low in seed produced by both farmers and local seed "experts", the latter were slightly more skilled at sorting out visibly affected seed (Sperling et al. 1995). A relatively low level of fungal bean pathogens was observed in samples from shops and markets located near FSEs (e.g., 1.8% for *Fusarium oxysorum* f. sp. *phaseoli*), but the level of infection in IBFA seed was negligible. Some samples from the seed enterprises showed relatively high levels of saprophytic infection, indicative of poor drying or storage.

The higher proportion of seed sorted out from the samples obtained from markets and shops compared with seed produced by IBFA (a mean of 36%, compared with 4%) (Buruchara and David 1995) further confirms the superiority of seed from specialized producers. It also highlights the monetary savings likely to be gained by farmers who buy from FSEs. This improved quality of FSE seed is attributed to the groups' use of better field and postharvest practices and skills (i.e., roguing, drying, sorting, and seed treatment).

Sale and promotion

Nearly all the seed produced by FSEs was sold locally, usually within 2 to 6 months after harvest, for 600-1200 Ugandan shillings (U Sh) per kilogram (i.e., US$0.66-$1.33 per kg). These prices are about two to three times higher than the lowest price of grain and comparable with, or higher than, the retail price of certified bean seed (U Sh 600-800 per kg). The quantities of seed purchased demonstrate the ability of FSEs to meet the specific needs of smallholders. More than 30% of Mbale buyers bought 3 or more kilos, and most Iganga farmers purchased smaller amounts, confirming differences among districts in demand for seed. Some buyers reserved seed in advance from the MWG because they prefer to buy just before planting to avoid the temptation of eating it. Because all transactions involved cash sales, FSEs do not appear to significantly facilitate the equitable spread of new varieties. In the short term, local (i.e., in nearby villages) demand for seed, 'CAL 96' in particular, was modest (IBFA) or high (MWG and BKTWG), but it remains to be seen if and how soon localized demand will decline. All groups sold 'CAL 96' more quickly than 'MCM 5001', but rejected the idea of charging a lower price for the latter variety to encourage sales.

Given fluctuating demand for seed, and in the absence of a specialized market for seed among Ugandan smallholders, seed entrepreneurs must actively engage in promotional and marketing activities. Although efforts in this area differed between groups, marketing was hardly ever a constraint, given the limited quantities of seed produced. The MWG gained visibility by participating in the district agricultural show (they won second prize) and even composed a song about the new varieties. The IBFA advertised its product at farmer meetings, through local authorities and traders, and sold seed through door-to-door canvassing, to schools, a rural development project, the district agricultural office and, on one occasion, to an NGO identified by CIAT. Factors accounting for slower sales by IBFA and BKTWG include:

Lower demand,

Limited promotional efforts,

Farmers' reluctance to buy 'MCM 5001' because of its small size and lack of markets,

High prices (IBFA),

Competition with free seed of the same varieties distributed by the Uganda National Bean Program (IBFA), and

Farmers' tendency to confuse 'CAL 96' with a local variety (IBFA).

All three FSEs showed little interest in selling seed to traders and seed merchants because these middlemen offered low prices.

Impact of seed enterprises

The impact of the three seed enterprises can be assessed at two levels: among producers, and in the wider community. In the absence of systematic, community, impact studies, observations by the two Mbale groups that most farmers in their respective villages had bought seed from them suggests favorable impact. A second area of impact is bound to develop from IBFA being involved in seed education.

Specialized seed production had a positive impact on the seed growers in the areas of financial improvement and empowerment. Earnings by the FSEs during the study surpassed income from traditional income-earning activities such as the sale of food crops: about US$1700 for IBFA, US$337 for BKTWG, and US$272 for MWG. In light of declining productivity after the first year, it is unclear whether continued production reflects perceived business profitability or other factors such as the prestige of working with researchers or having access to new varieties. Both women's groups felt they had satisfactorily achieved the objectives of the project, although compared with MWG, members of BKTWG rated their achievements more modestly. Both groups realized the need to increase production. They appreciated the participatory approach researchers used, noted members' increased confidence as a valued output of being involved in seed production, but identified the need for more training.

Lessons Learned from the Ugandan Case Studies and Future Challenges

Research on modalities for developing farmer seed enterprises provided valuable lessons and recommendations for eastern and southern Africa, as summarized below.

Organizational issues

Farmers can be trained, organized, and motivated to produce and market good quality bean seed. However, smallholders' capacity to produce seed efficiently and on a modest scale may be limited by their lack of resources (land, labor, and capital). Farmers who have the necessary resources (i.e., large-scale farmers) may be more capable of achieving modest production levels (>1-2 t/y).

The FSEs offer three main advantages over other provision approaches: sustainability by being market driven, possibilities for establishing linkages to formal institutions, and production of good quality seed—an issue of concern in areas of high disease pressure. This approach may not, however, be appropriate for all dissemination objectives or bean-growing environments. Table 3 outlines considerations of these factors and other approaches.

Smallholders' production and motivation to produce are influenced by the mode of organizing seed growing (individually versus communally) and arrangements for remunerating individual growers. An arrangement that allows for individual production and collective postharvest handling may be optimal from the production side, but for socioeconomic reasons may be unsuitable for certain farmers. Women seed growers face specific production constraints because of their limited access to resources (land, labor,

Table 3. Strategies and guidelines for selecting varietal dissemination approaches.

Objective	Strategy	Where appropriate	Concerns
Initiate varietal dissemination and promotion	Seed multiplication and marketing by formal institutions	Project-driven, quick impact needed	• Sustainable? • High establishment costs
Nonmarket-driven system for dissemination	Multiplication of <u>grain</u> by farmers working with formal institutions	Project-driven, quick impact needed	• Slow diffusion • Sustainable?
Sustainable, market-driven system for dissemination	• Small farmer seed enterprises (FSEs)	• High demand for seed	• External intervention needed
	• Small seed companies	• High disease pressure	• High establishment costs
	• Decentralized contract farming		
	• Micro-FSEs	• Medium-to-low demand for seed	• Technical supervision required
	• Support for existing farmer seed entrepreneurs	• High disease pressure	• Economic viability questionable

capital) and difficulties in controlling their own resources (labor, capital).

Repeated training on various aspects of seed production, agronomy, business skills, and marketing is key to successful enterprise development. To improve crop management, seed producers may also require close and regular field supervision by technical support staff for an initial period.

Supporting seed production efforts by farmers requires technical- and business-related expertise, and enormous time investments for monitoring producers and developing institutions and institutional linkages. Interested NGOs should initiate programs with technical support from NARS and international agricultural research centers (IARCs). The initial high cost needed to initiate such programs should pay off in the long term, assuming that the system is sustainable.

Although local demand exists for seed produced by specialized producers, FSEs must devise proactive marketing and promotion strategies aimed at larger markets to ensure long-term business success.

Policy issues

To encourage decentralized seed production, national seed authorities must designate a new class of seed with less stringent quality parameters (Table 4).

The "truthfully labeled" designation should be approved as an alternative to the existing system of centralized public certification. In this case, no field inspection is made, producers are wholly responsible for seed quality and are required to describe certain quality aspects on the label (Tripp and Van der Burg 1997). Alternatively, independent certification at a decentralized level can be explored (compare Garay et al. [nd] for the Bolivian case). Such a system might operate either by involving individuals (possibly extension agents), who have been trained by the public certification agency to inspect fields for artisanal quality seed, or by shifting the responsibility for quality control to an autonomous or local public institution.

Promoting farmer-led activities in seed production is challenging and no single approach or model exists for success. Key elements needed to ensure that FSEs successfully develop include:

Table 4. Quality parameters for improved[a] and certified bean seed in Uganda.

Parameters	Improved seed	Certified seed
Isolation (m)	5	5
Purity (by weight)	90%	99%
Germination (minimum)	80%	80%
Disease[b] levels (at final inspection)	HB, CBB, ANT: signs on leaves only BCMV: none	None
Moisture	13%	13%
Varietal purity	na[c]	99%
Off-types (maximum)	10/10,000	10/10,000

a. "Improved seed" is a designation proposed for artisanal production.
b. HB = halo blight; CBB = common bacterial blight; ANT = anthracnose; BCMV = bean common mosaic virus.
c. not applicable.

A range of superior varieties (from farmers' perspective) being regularly available;

Strong institutional support for some years to develop farmer capacity for seed production and small enterprise development, and to provide source seed;

A flexible quality control system; and

Formal institutional linkages to ensure these last two.

Figure 1 shows a conceptual model of the key linkages and institutions needed to establish a network of FSEs. The main features of the model may be summarized as follows:

1. Projects by NGOs are established in several areas of a country; NARS are closely involved in project design and provide technical training to project staff.

2. The project recruits, trains, advises, and monitors producers for 3 years. Where necessary, producers receive credit from independent credit facilities.

3. Producers obtain certified seed initially from the project, but later from the national seed company or on contract basis from commodity research programs.

4. Independent certification inspectors may inspect fields on a payment basis. The national seed authority authorizes and trains them.

5. Producers are organized into seed growers' associations, which arrange provision of source seed and other inputs, assist in marketing, and represent members' interests.

Avoiding the documented pitfalls of NGO involvement in seed production

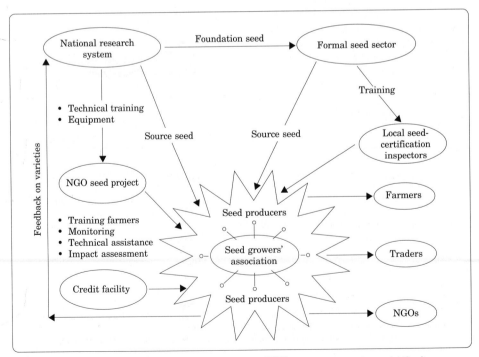

Figure 1. A conceptual model for farmer seed enterprises. (NGO = nongovernment organization.)

activities—lack of technical expertise, institutional linkages to research and seed agencies, and sustainability and the small scale of programs (Cromwell 1997; Wiggins and Cromwell 1995)—seriously challenges all agencies concerned with varietal promotion and seed production. Other commercial approaches, such as contract farming involving a partnership between traders, seed merchants, and farmers, have yet to be explored in eastern and southern Africa. Research institutions (both NARS and IARCs) can play a catalyzing role in addition to a technical role. For example, they could help other agencies design sustainable programs and establish informal, national agencies involved in community seed activity to avoid duplicating efforts, facilitate networking, coordinate nationalwide activities, and lobby for policy reforms.

Conclusions

The Ugandan case studies confirmed two important points. First, small-scale African farmers can be organized and motivated to produce and sell good-quality bean seed. Second, demand exists among smallholders for good quality seed of modern varieties supplied by specialized farmer producers. Although FSEs offer a sustainable solution to the problem of seed supply, the challenge of implementing this approach in eastern and southern Africa remains formidable. Collaborative linkages need to be fostered between farmers, researchers, NGOs, and the formal seed industry. Policy reforms need implementing and more client-oriented research systems institutionalizing.

As the model proposed here suggests, FSEs must be developed within the context of an integrated, seed supply system. This runs the spectrum from unspecialized seed production at the farm level to the formal seed industry, with each element playing well-defined, sometimes overlapping, roles. Guidelines offered in this paper need to be tested and new approaches devised in line with national conditions. It remains to be seen whether farmer-led, seed-provision systems can provide the impetus for revolutionizing national breeding procedures, varietal testing, and release systems and seed policy.

References

ADC/IDEA (Agribusiness Development Center and Investment in Developing Export Agriculture). 1996. A seed usage survey of maize and beans in six districts of Uganda. Kampala, Uganda. 33 p.

Almekinders C; Louwaars NP; de Bruijn GH. 1994. Local seed systems and their importance for an improved seed supply in developing countries. Euphytica 78:207-216.

Ashby J; Gracia T; Guerrero M; Quirós C; Roa J; and Beltrán J. 1995. Institutionalizing farmer participation in adaptive technology testing with the CIAL. Network paper 57. Agricultural Administration (Research and Extension) Network, Overseas Development Institute (ODI), London.

Bockari-Kubei S. 1994. The role of small-scale enterprises in African seed industries. Ph.D. dissertation. University of Reading, Reading, UK.

Buruchara R; David S. 1995. Seed quality: issues in small-scale farmer bean production. Paper presented at Southern Africa Development Community (SADC) Regional Bean Research Network Workshop, 2-4 October, Potchefstroom, South Africa.

Cromwell E. 1997. Local-level seed activities: opportunities and challenges for regulatory frameworks. In: Tripp R, ed. New seed and old laws: regulatory reform and the diversification of national seed systems. Intermediate Technology Publications, London. p 214-230.

Cromwell E; Wiggins S; Wentzel S. 1993. Sowing beyond the state: NGOs and seed supply in developing countries. Overseas Development Institute (ODI), London. 143 p.

David S. 1996. Local bean seed systems: preliminary results from surveys in two districts. In: David S, ed. Alternative approaches to bean seed production and distribution in eastern and southern Africa. Proc. working group meeting, 10-13 October, 1994, Kampala, Uganda. Africa Workshop Series, no. 32. CIAT, Kampala, Uganda. p 16-27.

David S; Kasozi S; Wortmann CS. 1997. An investigation of alternative bean seed marketing channels in Uganda. Network on Bean Research in Africa, Occasional Publication Series, no. 19. CIAT, Kampala, Uganda. 16 p.

Gaifami A. 1992. Developing local seed production in Mozambique. In: Cooper D; Vellve R; Hobbelink H, eds. Growing diversity, genetic resources and local food security. Intermediate Technology Publications, London. p 97-105.

Garay A; Pattie P; Landivar J; Rosales J. nd. Setting a seed industry in motion: a nonconventional, successful approach in a developing country. Working document no. 57. CIAT, Cali, Colombia. (In press.)

Groosman T; Linnemann A; Wierema H. 1991. Seed industry development in North-South perspective. Centrum voor Landbouwpublikaties en Landbouwdocumentatie (PUDOC), Wageningen, Netherlands. 107 p.

Hendersen PA; Singh R. 1990. NGO-government links in seed production: case studies from the Gambia and Ethiopia. Network paper 14. Agricultural Administration (Research and Extension) Network, Overseas Development Institute (ODI), London. p 1-27.

Lépiz R; Ashby J; Roa J. 1996. Artisanal bean production in Latin America. In: David S, ed. Alternative approaches to bean seed production and distribution in eastern and southern Africa. Proc. working group meeting, 10-13 October, 1994, Kampala, Uganda. Africa Workshop Series, no. 32. CIAT, Kampala, Uganda. p 101-112.

Sperling L; Scheidegger U; Buruchara R. 1995. Enhancing small farm seed systems: principles derived from bean research in the Great Lakes Region. Network on Bean Research in Africa, Occasional Publication Series, no. 15. CIAT, Kampala, Uganda. 30 p.

Tripp R; Van der Burg W. 1997. The conduct and reform of seed quality control. In: Tripp R, ed. New seed and old laws: regulatory reform and the diversification of national seed systems. Intermediate Technology Publications, London. p 121-154.

Wachtel E. 1976. A farm of one's own: the rural orientation of women's group enterprises in Nakuru, Kenya. Rural Africana 29:69-80.

Wiggins S; Cromwell E. 1995. NGOs and seed provision to smallholders in developing countries. World Develop 23:413-422.

CHAPTER 12

Institutional Innovation as an Entry Point for System-Level Technological Change

*J. Ashby**

Introduction

Adoption of new technology is a particular problem in natural resource management (NRM), where a lack of property rights may mean that stakeholders other than the adopters capture the benefits of new technologies. Intervention to bring about institutional change can improve NRM, encourage the adoption of technical advances, and provide incentives to undertake research.

Technical innovation stimulates institutional change, whether it arises exogenously or as a result of an endogenous search for advantage, and is fostered or constrained by institutional structure. Institutional rules can allow the benefits of technical advances to be fully used, and are important in generating technological change.

Farmers and resource users are in a much better position to know the problems they face, while scientists are particularly skilful in making the linkages between those problems and their underlying causes, and in developing alternative solutions. Farmers have strong incentives to select from among the research results those new varieties, technologies, or techniques that best meet their needs in the local environments. In these circumstances, the potential users sometimes do not adopt technical advances that would improve agricultural productivity or NRM. The constraints to adoption must be identified, and if possible overcome, to realize the research gains.

At the same time, the institutional structure itself influences technical change, providing incentives for technical advances or stifling scientific enquiry (North 1991). Rules that allow innovators to reap the rewards of their work will stimulate technical change. Mechanisms that allow farmers to communicate their need to public agencies will help lead to solutions that are likely to be adopted.

Devolving responsibility to local organizations is increasingly attractive to governments. Decentralization gives local agencies the responsibility for decision making and payment for services. This is expected to improve and democratize the provision of services at the local level (Putnam 1993). Strengthening farmer experimentation represents a local capacity for adaptive agricultural research and technology development. Such devolution can improve the effectiveness of agricultural research

* CIAT, Cali, Colombia.

and development (R&D) to serve resource-poor farmers (Ashby and Sperling 1995).

Farmer experimentation requires organizational and methodological support. However, strengthening farmer capacity for experimentation and technology development is different to including farmers in programs run by agencies external to the farming community. For these reasons, institutional innovation may be a prerequisite to adoption of new technologies whether this is productivity enhancing or resource-conserving technology. Designing new institutions has therefore to be considered as part of a systems approach. This paper looks at two examples. One is at the landscape scale: the intervention in the watershed of the Ovejas River in Colombia. The other is at the community level: the work of the Committees for Local Agricultural Research (CLARs). Both illustrate the broader problem of institutional change as a precondition for technology adoption.

The Pilot Area

The projects were initiated in a pilot area in the Department of Cauca, in southern Colombia—one of the poorest, lowest-wage departments in the country. The area chosen is characterized by hilly terrain, poor roads and markets, and small farms, averaging 5 ha in size (average cultivated area is less than 3 ha). All farms engage in a mix of commercial and subsistence production. This is a marginal coffee production area with infertile, often badly eroded, acid soils. Most farmers cultivate coffee, together with cassava, as a cash crop; some maize and climbing beans are traditionally grown for subsistence. Livestock are scarce (only 13% of farms

have cattle), although the typical farm may have as much as 40%-60% of its area in degraded pasture or secondary brush fallow, a feature of the rotation commonly practiced.

Objectives

Both the examples examined in this paper involved participation that requires farmers to assume greater responsibility for making decisions, allocating resources, and implementing activities—a type of participation that is often called "empowering". The main objective of the CLAR project was to assess whether community-based research committees could take over adaptive research from formal research systems, and improve on this service by making it more relevant to farmers' needs.

The Ovejas River intervention shows the relationship between technical change and institutional innovation. An important objective was to create a forum in which local inhabitants of the watershed could define, monitor, and enforce their own rules for managing natural resources in the watershed, and determine which benefits to go to which stakeholders. The existing institutional structure of the hillside agroecosystem prevented effective NRM, the adoption of technologies, and the design of technical research programs.

A most important question addressed was to what extent this type of "empowering" farmer participation in research could be scaled up to achieve broad coverage, and at what cost. Before participatory research became fashionable, critics often queried whether this approach was an expensive luxury, attractive on a case-by-case basis and when supported by highly skilled professionals, but not affordable for working with large numbers of farmers (Farrington and Martin 1993).

Problems Addressed

Natural resource management

The Cabuyal River is one of five main tributaries feeding the Ovejas River, which, in turn, runs into the Cauca River, an important source of water and hydroelectric power for the city of Cali, located downstream in the Cauca Valley. The quality of water in the Ovejas River was poor because of pollution from heavy silting from upstream clearing and deforestation and consequent soil erosion, agrochemicals, waste products from artisanal coffee postharvest processing, and runoff of organic fertilizer (heavily used by small-scale farmers in tributary watersheds).

The erosion in the upper areas of the watershed is a major cause of annual flooding problems in the lower lying areas. The biological and agrochemical pollution of the water was especially marked in areas where vegetable and bean crops were cultivated, or where coffee and cassava were processed. This was seen as a serious problem for urban users in the Cauca Valley. Also, piped water for community use and irrigation purposes was less available lower down the hillsides and in the Valley because of the clearing and deforestation in the upper reaches.

Technical change

Techniques available to improve the quality and quantity of downstream water included practices such as enclosing areas along river banks and around springs where natural vegetation could reestablish itself, and planting contour barriers to control soil erosion. Upland farmers had little incentive to adopt any of these practices, however, because they bore the costs while the benefits accrued to

downstream users (Ashby et al. 1998). Although external agencies concerned with NRM saw bad soil management practices in the area as a major problem, farmers were more concerned with the poor availability of credit, which made fertilizer difficult to obtain.

Institutional change

The institutional structure promoted the inefficient and inequitable use of the watershed's natural resources. The water catchment was used as a typical open access resource with each party in the area acting solely in its own interest, resulting in overuse and deterioration. Downstream users had no established rights to either the quantity or quality of water from the higher levels of the catchment. Upstream users were able to impose significant externalities on downstream users at no cost to themselves.

Attempts by the Corporación Autónoma Regional del Valle del Cauca (CVC), a local governmental agency for the environment, to control resource use by upland farmers, were seen to be imposed by downstream interest groups and unfair; they were usually ineffective. Opportunities to internalize the externalities of poor land use were limited in the upper reaches of the watershed, although wealthy sugarcane producers in the Valley bought land in the tributary watersheds to reforest and to protect their water sources and minimize flooding.

With no defined rights to use the natural resources, no mechanism existed to resolve conflicts. Those adversely affected by externalities had little recourse other than violence or force. Thus, conflict among different stakeholder groups was common because they sought to exert rights to natural resources. The capacity for conflict resolution was limited because existing authorities, such as the indigenous Indian *cabildo*, had an unrecognized jurisdiction and no ability to enforce agreements.

The indigenous Indian communities in the upper reaches of the watershed burned the land to clear it. This was a perennial source of problems for downstream users of water (Castaño et al. 1995; Ravnborg and Ashby 1996). Yet no mechanism was in place to voice these concerns or to resolve the problem of water availability downstream. Nor was there an accepted forum for resolving conflicts about land rights. The loss of traditional property rights to Indian land through colonization by mestizos has resulted in endemic conflict, in the absence of generally recognized formal mechanisms of enforcement, and redress.

The existing institutional structure provided little information to stakeholders on the causes and effects of poor land use, the size and distribution of costs and benefits, or potential solutions (IDB 1995; Knapp et al. 1995). The status of soil, water, and vegetation of concern could not be monitored. As a result, no feedback could be given on the relative costs and benefits that could motivate those adversely affected to make institutional change.

Stakeholders had no common perception of the problems (Ravnborg and Ashby 1996). Inhabitants of the lower and mid-altitude watershed communities were concerned about the seasonal scarcity of piped water, the disappearance of streams, and the decreasing water flow in the river. They attributed this to deforestation by the inhabitants in the upper watershed. The agencies responsible to downstream users were concerned about water quality in the Cauca Valley. In contrast, the upper-watershed communities saw their major problems as lack of schools, electricity, all-weather roads, and health services.

No structure existed (e.g., as with an elected watershed users' association) to allow individuals to negotiate institutional change. The stakeholders who might have common interests were poorly identified and there was little, if any, formal organization that would allow them to collectively promote change. Only the local water board was available for local organizations to participate in NRM.

Independent organizations with different objectives managed the resources of the watershed. The water board managed the piped water supply drawn from the headwaters of the tributary watersheds, and the CVC was responsible for conserving forest reserves around the aqueduct intakes. No formal channels were in place for any joint decision making or coordination.

Also, various external agencies concerned with NRM and agriculture were active within the catchment area but had differing agricultural or conservation objectives and no incentive to coordinate their technical assistance and conservation efforts with each other, public agencies, or local communities. Agricultural development programs promoted credit, technical assistance, and commercialization outlets. Upland farmers were thus provided with incentives to clear and burn secondary bush fallow and forests to plant cassava—notorious locally for its effects on soil degradation.

The Cabuyal Watershed Project

Partners and beneficiaries

Research to develop a model of participatory watershed management was initiated in 1993 in the Cabuyal catchment of the Ovejas River watershed, through the Interinstitutional Consortium for Sustainable Agriculture in the Hillsides (CIPASLA, its Spanish acronym), and the creation of a watershed users' association. A key function of the latter was to manage a sizeable portion of the project budget to cofinance or wholly support activities to stimulate local responsibility for improving NRM in the watershed. The formulation and sponsorship of projects by the watershed users was intended to articulate local demand for rural development and other services to the external organizations now under the auspices of CIPASLA (CIAT 1995).

The watershed users' association was formally constituted as the Federation of Beneficiaries of the Cabuyal Watershed (FEBESURCA, its Spanish acronym). The local leaders, active in promoting the association, defined the basis for membership as representation of all the different local organizations and interest groups, not necessarily all formally organized. The membership reflected the perception of the local leadership elite that FEBESURCA would be a pressure group composed of people like themselves, who could be expected both to mobilize local support and to interact effectively with external organizations.

Problem diagnosis

To identify problems of the watershed, an interinstitutional coordinating committee was formed with representatives from the public sector, nongovernment organizations (NGOs), and grower associations to collate available information and make a joint diagnosis. The committee, in consultation with local extension agents and community leaders familiar with the Ovejas River watershed, selected the Cabuyal River as a pilot catchment area for diagnosis and subsequent intervention. The boundaries of the watershed were set to include all those able to appropriate water from the Cabuyal River, thus defining the stakeholders and providing the boundary for users' rights and obligations.

Project development

Local community negotiations to define, monitor, and enforce property rights in the uplands began to replace externally imposed (but usually flouted) regulations. The formation of CIPASLA enabled the local community to initiate a change in the institutional arrangements to establish conservation zones in the upper reaches of the watershed. Previously, the CVC had been unable to implement its longstanding program to enclose buffer zones to regenerate forests around watercourses. The local water board and the regional watershed users' authority, together with the community leaders (particularly the cassava growers and horticultural growers cooperatives), began to work with the upper watershed inhabitants, on whose land were located the springs and streams feeding the water reservoirs. The FEBESURCA leaders persuaded the CVC to relax their recommendations for enclosing and protecting the forest and for regenerating natural forest cover around these water sources. The CVC provided technical support, but relaxed its exclusive hold on local monitoring and sanctioning, delegating this to the local water board.

This arrangement enabled community leaders to negotiate with the upper watershed farmers as to mutually acceptable limits on the use of these areas for agriculture. FEBESURCA, through the local water board, organized community labor drawn from upper and lower watershed communities to plant trees and enclose areas to be protected by mutual agreement. Within 18 months, 135 ha were enclosed along the main watercourse and tributary streams, and 150,000 trees planted. The community contributed 3714 person-days. They explained their motivation for working together as investing in their children's future, for whom the availability of water will be critical. The local water board also announced that they would turn off access to piped water for those families failing to contribute to community labor.

In early 1993, community leaders began visiting different areas of the watershed to motivate local people to collaborate in improving watershed management. They focused their campaign on decreasing water availability, which they associated with deforestation of the upper reaches of the watercourses.

The group organized a series of task forces to visit communities in the upper reaches. This was the first time many had gone to these communities. The task forces found much greater poverty than in the lower altitudes: impassable cart-tracks, an absence of schools, low quality housing, poor crops, and an extensive wasteland of bracken-covered fallow left after shifting cultivation. The farmers in the upper watershed described their problems and concerns and explained how the clearing and cutting of trees around the reservoirs provided not only cropland, but also charcoal, almost their only source of cash.

At the same time, the external organizations in the coordinating committee began to develop a common set of objectives and activities to achieve them, consolidating efforts behind the evolving agenda of the community leaders. At a planning workshop in March 1993, the participants identified a joint program in which each institution had a defined role and contribution. It was agreed that conservation activities required complementary agricultural, production, and commercialization activities, mirroring community plans to compensate upland farmers. Each organization began to identify its activities as complementary with those of others.

At this workshop CIPASLA was formed by the 12 participant organizations and was charged with formalizing agreements among them and raising funds for the joint program. By mid-1993, CIPASLA had developed a budget from outside grants, participating organizations, and the participating communities. FEBESURCA had its own share of this budget and provided a forum for local organizations to define an agenda to present to the external organizations in the form of community-based projects. This institutional structure represented a more interdependent arrangement than had existed previously. It led to the development of a supply-driven portfolio of projects offered by the external organizations. However, it was now organized in a way that made the opportunities for joint or complementary action more readily apparent. The projects that were most rapidly executed were those that met the demand of the mid-altitude farmers to protect their water supply from the upper watershed. These projects were carried out with the participation of local organizations, such as the local water board, and the leadership of farmer cooperatives.

Adoption of soil conservation practices

An example of successfully involving farmers in decision making was in their adoption of soil conservation practices. For more than 10 years, the CVC and the Coffee Federation recommended coffee and cassava growers to plant live barriers incorporating citronella (*Cymbopogon nardus*) and "limoncillo" (lemon grass, *C. citratus*), but with little success. Virtually no spontaneous adoption of live barriers occurred.

The CVC extension agents were trained in methods of participatory technology evaluation (Ashby 1990) and agreed to allow farmers flexibility in choosing whether and how to establish live contour barriers. Initially, local community members selected the farmers to participate as being interested in experimenting with soil conservation practices. After 1992, participants were volunteers.

Although some farmers were willing to experiment with the technically "best" option, vetiver grass, their criteria for accepting live contour barriers were primarily related to the short-term utility they could gain from the materials included in them. Farmers previously uninterested in planting contour barriers accepted a cut-and-carry forage grass barrier. They also selected sugarcane as a useful component for live barriers. Once these materials were made available, farmers were willing to pay for planting materials to establish the barriers.

Involving farmers in making decisions about soil conservation recommendations catalyzed a process of farmer-to-farmer transfer of information about the optional practices. Spontaneous adoption began. In the pilot area where participatory evaluations were tested, the number of farmers who established barriers, independent of any credit incentive, increased dramatically from two farmers in 1991 to 261 by 1994.

Benefits of participatory approaches

The involvement of community leaders in the participatory problem diagnosis initiated a change in their strategy to promote conservation of the remaining forest around the reservoirs. They began to seek support from external organizations via the coordinating committee for programs to improve the quality of life in the upper watershed as an explicit reward for the commitment of upland farmers to cease cutting and clearing. They also began to formulate plans for lower watershed farmers to teach the upland farmers how to improve their crops and to discuss ways in which the farmer cooperatives could promote the marketing of produce grown in the upper watershed.

A quid pro quo relationship had emerged that enabled communities in the upper and middle levels to work together. In effect, downstream users bought the right to a continued water supply by restricting the rights of upland farmers to use damaging land-use practices. Improvements in production and income-generating technology and infrastructure in the upper regions bought the protection of water sources. Although the value of water and conservation, and of technology and infrastructure, was not measured, a working consensus had been built about what was worthwhile to the different stakeholders involved.

Lessons learned

Although the project has been operating for only 2 years, lessons have already been learned about institutional intervention. The project provided the means for collective action by reducing transactional costs both to the disparate agencies active within the watershed and to the local watershed communities. This provided a climate for mutually beneficial and peaceful negotiation among interested parties. Watershed users had relatively few competing interests, which reduced the costs of negotiation and made a successful outcome more likely. Also, the interests of mid-altitude farmers for water availability and of downstream users for water quality were relatively homogenous, reducing the likelihood of splits within the interest group, promoting commonality, and encouraging them to work together. Although the upper watershed farmers did not have a common interest in water, negotiation permitted their needs to be met while addressing the concerns of users in the lower reaches. The changes in NRM practices in the uplands was negotiated among the interested parties rather than enforced by outside authorities. Thus, the new practices were more likely to reflect the needs of local people in the local environment.

The constraints to the adoption of technological innovations that could improve NRM were identified. The programs of external agencies with conflicting aims tended to preserve incentives to degrade land, and the adoption of costly practices that benefited downstream users had no incentives. Introducing compensation for improved land-use practices, and providing new market opportunities and infrastructure, gave upland farmers incentives to adopt conservation practices such as contour planting and to take part in adaptive research.

The institutional intervention has to date resulted in establishing a strong mechanism for local action and negotiation to improve NRM. It has permitted the definition of the resources to be managed, those who use them or are affected by their use, and those who can be excluded from using them (Ravnborg and Ashby 1996). With this information, all the stakeholders in the natural resource base are well known and can take part in the negotiation of institutional change. By identifying gainers and losers, it allows losers to be compensated. It has provided local people with "social capital" that enables them to recognize their interdependence and to work cooperatively for their mutual benefit.

This social capital consists of the shared expectations, commonly accepted rules of conduct, and recognized sanctions and rewards that a group of people develop in a joint activity (Ostrom 1994). The institutional structure has emphasized the interdependence of interests and individuals. By promoting face-to-face interaction, the transactional costs of negotiating change are low. The new institutional structure has begun a process for generating and acquiring knowledge and information about the resources to be managed, the technological innovation opportunities, and the behavior of users and beneficiaries. It also includes a nascent forum for conflict resolution.

Although the project has been active for only a short period, the results for improved NRM are encouraging. Buffer zones have been created around water sources, trees have been planted, and burning controlled. Upland farmers have begun to change their land management practices. Improvements in the quantity and quality of downstream water are anticipated.

Technology Testing with CLARs

Problem diagnosis

Participatory diagnosis is a crucial feature of the work of CLARs because it identifies the priorities for their research agenda. If this diagnosis captures the topics of importance to most farmers, then the research that the CLAR carries out has a good chance of being widely relevant.

During 1986-1988, the Participatory Research in Agriculture (IPRA, mixed language acronym) project conducted a study of farmer experimentation in the pilot area. A systematic random sample of 30% was drawn from a household census covering 16 communities in the study area. The survey documented over 1000 informal experiments recalled by farmers. The communities were classified into three types: primarily subsistence production, mixed subsistence and commercial production, and primarily commercial. The study showed a wealth of informal experimentation by farmers, who were not linked with formal research and extension, in every farm type.

Project development

Based on the IPRA study, the project identified a need to mobilize local leadership among experimenting farmers to encourage them to work together and exchange their research and its results. To assess the effects of different linkages with external institutions, the project formed CLARs in three different institutional contexts: directly in local communities, with already existing informal groups formed by NGOs for credit and extension purposes, and with farmer associations or cooperatives.

In 1990, the process of forming committees began in Colombia in four farmer associations or cooperatives and one community with no cooperative. The five "pilot" committees first developed methodologies and training materials. In the pilot area, the number of committees increased to 18 in late 1991, 32 in 1992-1993, and 55 by early 1995. Additional committees were formed in Colombia, Bolivia, Ecuador, Brazil, Peru, Nicaragua, El Salvador, Guatemala, and Honduras, bringing the total to almost 300 in late 1997.

The farmer research committees have resulted in action-research through a continuous learning process. Monitoring and evaluation of the development of each committee is an important activity of the project team, and of the committees themselves. Just as in the Ovejas River watershed organization, building social capital is an essential ingredient of successful technical innovation.

Results

The results derived from monitoring CLARs in the pilot area show that the 48 CLARs, with a decreasing amount of institutional support, have carried out a large and increasing number of on-farm trials. Farmers consider these trials, which are, to a large extent, statistically analyzable, useful for knowledge generation.

A rapid appraisal of the CLARs' impact showed that, in 75% of the participating communities, new seed, new cultural practices, or information about recommendations were perceived as benefits. For example, one community asked its research committee to compare a local practice for controlling nematodes with the state agency's recommendation to cover the ground under fruit bushes with black plastic. The CLAR experiment shows that the local practice is more effective under farmer management.

State institutions in the pilot area set research and extension priorities on the basis of the area devoted to different crops in the municipality. The priorities in the pilot area are cassava, pasture, sugarcane, and coffee. Small-scale farmers participating in the CLARs' diagnostic meetings had different priorities, as shown by the crops selected for CLAR experiments (Table 1). The communities identified a more diverse research agenda than the institutions. For example, not one community prioritized cassava in their group diagnosis, although over 4000 farmers participated in such community meetings.

The CLAR agenda reflects farmers' objectives to identify alternatives to the traditional cash crops of coffee and cassava. It also reflects their aim to increase their food sufficiency by growing staples such as potatoes, beans (a substitute for meat in the rural diet), and maize. Maize is used for feeding chickens; it is an important source of locally produced protein, and an important ingredient of traditional staple dishes. Although these staples are produced in Cauca, the Department imports them from other parts of the country to meet its food requirements (SAG 1989), thus reflecting a regional problem in local food self-sufficiency.

The 55 CLARs operating by early 1995 in the Department of Cauca were scattered in nine municipalities, which together comprise an area of 6648 km², with an average population density of 40 persons per km². The farming communities participating in the project occupy an area of about 1605 km², in which the average

Table 1.   Experiments conducted by 48 Committees for Local Agricultural Research (CLARs) in the Department of Cauca, Colombia.

Topic	Number of experiments[a]		
	Phase I (pilot)	Phase II (1992/93)	Phase III (1993/94)
Peas and related cultural practices	1	3	5
Potato	6	5	3
Maize and related cultural practices	7	8	7
Peanut	1	3	4
Fruits and related fertilizer dosages, pest control	3	6	11
Beans	6	4	0
Snap beans	0	1	1
Tomato	1	1	1
Soya bean	1	2	1
Sugarcane	1	1	1
Vegetables	4	7	6
Chicken feed mixes	1	1	0
Forage grasses	1	1	1
Cover crops (green manure)	0	0	1
Guinea pigs	0	0	1
Total	33	43	43

a.   The number of experiments is smaller than the number of CLARs because not all CLARs established new experiments.

population density can be as high as 132 persons per km^2, particularly if the extensive cattle and forest holdings are not included. Communities are characterized by a land use of 0.25 ha of cropland per capita, a figure comparable with estimates for Bolivia (0.33 ha cropland per capita), Ecuador (0.25), or Peru (0.17) (Pachico et al. 1994).

Since 1991, the CLARs in the project area have met annually, for 1 or 2 days, to exchange results. This meeting is financed by the communities raising money for the transport and lodging of attending members. The CLARs report on their experiments, exchange seed, swap notes about their host institutions, and formulate recommendations on how to better meet the goals they establish in each meeting. This experience first prompted the election of a central coordinating committee in 1993, then, in 1994, led to the CLARs' decision to form a corporation, the CLAR Corporation. Donations were obtained to establish an investment fund from which the Corporation could draw up to 70% of the interest for operating expenses; the remaining interest returned to the capital. This put the CLARs on a self-sustaining financial basis. In addition, the Corporation's paraprofessionals began giving courses to the municipal extension services (Unidades Municipales de Asistencia Técnica Agropecuaria or UMATAs), which contracted them to form small numbers of pilot CLARs elsewhere. The UMATAs pay as much as 50% of the paraprofessionals' salaries, thus generating additional income for the Corporation.

Additional benefits

Some of the CLARs that had successfully selected new, locally adapted, crop varieties evolved into small seed-production enterprises to meet local demand. Six CLARs in the pilot area have begun to produce seed, for which they receive additional training in simple seed production, processing, and quality control techniques. The seed is distributed locally through village stores and weekend markets. An estimated 281 ha of maize, 3064 ha of beans, and 7 ha of field peas (an entirely new crop introduced by CLAR experimentation into the pilot area) have been planted with CLAR seed.

More than 10,000 farmers have purchased CLAR seed, which, over one planting season, is estimated to have produced grain to a gross value of more than US$2 million. Based on the yield differential between locally available varieties and those selected and produced by the CLARs, use of the seed represents an additional US$765,000 of gross income from maize and beans, and over US$8,000 from peas. On a per capita basis, for farmers who purchased CLAR seed, this represents an increment worth about 1 month's wages in one planting season.

Developing small business enterprises was not part of the original design for the farmer research committees. Not all CLARs evolved into seed producers. Indeed, many do not test varieties, but select cultural practices, fertilizer rates, or animal diet as their topics of experimentation. Much of the knowledge generated by CLAR experiments shows that local practice is as good or better in terms of farmers' criteria as outsiders' recommendations. Knowledge generation remains, therefore, the main business of the CLARs.

Nonetheless, the income-generation opportunities that the seed enterprises provide are a powerful incentive to CLARs' research. This is the "development" part of their R&D and faces the weakest institutional support. "Venture capital" is difficult to obtain to finance scaling-up from a successful experiment to commercial production. The CLAR fund, as mentioned, supports only small-scale experimentation.

The seed enterprises also generate employment because they must hire additional labor to plant, harvest, sort, clean, and pack the seed in 1 to 5 kg sacks, also made locally by women. The bean seed enterprises have, for example, generated an average of 20,000 labor-days of employment over five seasons—worth an estimated US$85,000 at current wage rates over the 5 years of operation.

Six CLARs formed early in the project achieved this impact. There is no guarantee that the newer CLARs will repeat this experience by identifying new practices or germplasm. The six that have developed into seed enterprises may have already captured the best opportunity and the windfall profits from participatory breeding and seed production. The impact of the newer CLARs may be more difficult to realize, especially as their research agenda is shifting emphasis from grains to perishables (Table 1). But the recent introduction of field peas, via CLAR experimentation, suggests that there could be scope for a significant increase in impact from CLAR experimentation with high-value crops.

Assessing costs

Few published data are available on the costs of doing adaptive research with groups of farmers. Table 2 shows the total operating cost per CLAR (i.e., per community per year) at US$502. The annual per capita cost ranges from US$125 (when considering only the 220 farmers who are committee members) to under US$1 based on the total

population in the area of influence. Annual per capita cost is US$6.5, assuming that only one-third of the population in each community is in contact with their CLAR's adaptive testing. Based on the estimated number of purchasers of CLAR seed, the cost per capita would be about US$3. The total annual operating budget of the CLAR Corporation currently amounts to the equivalent of about two agronomists' salaries at national program rates.

The cost data presented here should not be viewed as conclusive. Further testing of the approach without the intervention of the IPRA project team is under way. This will permit assessment of how robust and replicable the method is in different environments with variant cost structures.

Table 2. Annual operating costs of the Committee for Local Agricultural Research (CLAR) Corporation for 55 CLARs, Department of Cauca, Colombia.

Costs	US$
Annual (per CLAR)	
Personnel costs[a]	290.00
Cost of experiment[b]	90.00
Other[c]	122.00
Total	502.00
Per capita	**(per year)**
Total population (50,000)	0.55
CLAR communities (12,900 people)	2.10
33% of CLAR communities (4,260 people)	6.50
Seed purchasers (10,500)	2.60
CLAR members (220)	125.50

a. Includes agronomist (one-third time), farmer coordinator (full-time), paraprofessionals (2 full-time).
b. Average of costs per CLAR charged against CLAR funds in 1994.
c. Average of transportation, supplies, and capital depreciation on four motorcycles.

Conclusions

The case studies show that institutional change is an important stimulus, and that technical innovation improved NRM in particular. The baseline study of farmer experimentation identified a wealth of informal testing carried out by resource-poor farmers in the pilot area. This informal research was unrecognized by the state and the local NGO programs; and the knowledge generated by individual farmers was perceived by each as something to be guarded rather than to be shared with the community at large. The CLARs are an institutional innovation that enabled farmers to acquire and exchange new knowledge, stimulating technical change. The watershed users' association provided a new institutional arrangement that allowed downstream communities to negotiate rights to natural resources with upper watershed farmers to improve the quality and quantity of downstream water, while compensating them for restricting their customary usage. It also encouraged the adoption of new technology and created incentives for the community to participate in adaptive research.

CLARs are a mechanism through which communities can give the local experimenters a public identity and a role that incurs respect and status in the community, and in links with external agencies. The results show that a fully trained CLAR can manage the adaptive research trials required for the research agenda identified in the 48 participating communities. The experimental results have been useful for knowledge generation, have contributed to increasing the diversity of technology tested, and have improved the flow of technologies to the participating communities. This has brought sizeable monetary benefits in the specific case of CLAR seed purchasers.

References

Ashby J. 1990. Evaluating technology with farmers: a handbook. Investigación Participativa en Agricultura/ *Participatory Research in Agriculture* (IPRA), CIAT, Cali, Colombia. 95 p.

Ashby J; Sperling L. 1995. Institutionalizing participatory, client-driven research and technology development in agriculture. Dev Change 26:753-770.

Ashby J; Gracia T; Guerrero MP; Quirós J; Roa I. 1998. Supporting farmer experimentation with Local Agricultural Research Committees. In: van Veldhuizen L; Johnson DA; Thompson J, eds. Farmers' research in practice: lessons from the field. Intermediate Technology Publications, London. p 245-261.

Castaño J; Ostertag CF; Patiño CA; Smith J. 1995. Market opportunities linked to erosion control practices: a key to adoption? In: Hillsides Program annual report 1994-1995. CIAT, Cali, Colombia. p 101-128.

CIAT. 1995. Hillsides Program annual report 1993-1994. Cali, Colombia. 324 p.

Farrington J; Martin A. 1993. Farmer participation in agricultural research: a review of concepts and practices. Agricultural Administration Unit, Occasional Paper no. 9. Overseas Development Institute (ODI), London. 79 p.

IDB (Inter-American Development Bank). 1995. Concepts and issues in watershed management. Working paper no. 2. Evaluation Office, Washington, DC. 26 p.

Knapp EB; Rubiano JE; Hansen JW. 1995. Decision support systems for land use planning and technology design. In: Hillsides Program annual report 1993-1994. CIAT, Cali, Colombia. p 71-85.

North D. 1991. Institutional innovation and agricultural development: constraints, problems, promise. Paper presented at the Institutional Innovations for Sustainable Agricultural Development Conference, Oct 14-18, Bellagio, Italy.

Ostrom E. 1994. Constituting social capital and collective action. J Theor Politics 4:343-562.

Pachico D; Ashby JA; Sanint LR. 1994. Natural resource and agricultural prospects for the hillsides of Latin America. In: Hillsides Program annual report, 1993-1994. CIAT, Cali, Colombia. p 283-321.

Putnam RD. 1993. The prosperous community: social capital and public life. Am Prospect 13:35-42.

Ravnborg HM; Ashby J. 1996. Organizing for local-level watershed management: lessons from the Río Cabuyal watershed, Colombia. Network Paper no. 65. Overseas Development Institute (ODI), London. p 1-14.

SAG (Sociedad de Agricultores y Ganaderos del Valle del Cauca). 1989. El Cauca: Tierras de progreso. Cali, Colombia.

CHAPTER 13

Conclusions: Participatory Systems Research, Toward the Future

*Sam Fujisaka**

Perhaps the general theme of the chapters in this volume is how agricultural research is striving to make problem-solving more effective and efficient through simultaneously integrating germplasm and natural resource management (NRM) research, continuously developing and applying farmer participatory research (FPR) approaches, and establishing new forms of team and partnership research. The chapters provide a clear view of what has been achieved and reasons for successes and failures. Expected future impacts are implicit in much of the work, as are strategies needed to achieve them.

Integration of Germplasm and NRM Research

The projects described indicate substantial progress in the integration of germplasm and NRM research. Researchers are introducing new forage materials, especially legumes, and small-scale farmers in Asia and Africa are testing and using them as green manure, cover crops, and improved fallow rotations. These uses of forages in low-input systems seek to improve nutrient cycling, maintain soil structure, combat weeds, and reduce soil erosion. In the Latin American savannas and forest margins, researchers are working with farmers and ranchers to develop animal feeding systems that are both more productive and more sustainable through the introduction and farmer testing of new forage mixtures. Work on integrated crop-livestock systems based largely on new multipurpose legumes in the savannas has sought to solve problems associated with low soil fertility, pasture degradation, soil compaction and erosion, build-up of pests and weeds, and water contamination. Farmer participatory research in cassava-based systems in Latin America and Asia has successfully combined the testing of new cassava varieties with soil erosion control and integrated crop and pest management.

Successes have been based on:

1. Research commitment to integrating germplasm and NRM research and to form needed multidisciplinary teams.

2. Sufficient resources to support long-term germplasm and strategic research.

3. Availability of seed or planting materials of new varieties or cultivars identified as potentially appropriate for farmers' systems.

---

* CIAT, Cali, Colombia.

155

4. The natural willingness of farmers to test new varieties.

The last, in turn, can be an incentive to participate in the testing of NRM innovations. Also implicit in the research presented is that successful systems research is conducted in carefully selected appropriate benchmark or reference sites in targeted agroecosystems. The agroecosystems that CIAT targets are forest margins, Latin American hillsides, and Latin American savannas. Although research is conducted at levels ranging from farm to agroecosystem, much of the fieldwork is done at the watershed level.

Failures are less clear. CIAT's commitment to integrated germplasm-NRM research (i.e., to systems research) has contributed directly to the shaping of the systems projects described in this volume. The papers show how the NARS partners were conducting systems research in these same projects, but do not indicate if changes of approach from separate research on germplasm/commodity and NRM to integrated research was taking place in NARS as a whole. The implicit, desirable impact for the future would be the NARS' adoption of systems approaches; and the similarly implicit strategy would be to continue and strengthen partnership research and demonstrate the successes of systems research.

Participatory Research

The chapters reveal a range of participatory approaches; such that, taken together, the development over time of such approaches is evident. The FPR approaches include:

1. Selected farmers individually conduct trials and provide feedback to researchers. Treatments are largely researcher-designed. In the case of the Colombian forest margins, this initial FPR led to other farmer-initiated experimentation.

2. Individual farmers test researcher-developed innovations (e.g., for soil erosion control). At the same time, researchers in the Cauca Valley tried to make the adoption of soil erosion control measures more economically attractive by assisting in the commercialization of new products resulting from adoption. Cassava researchers in Asia also supplied innovations more immediately attractive to farmers (new varieties and management options) for testing as a way to generate interest in soil conservation.

3. A committee for local agricultural research, selected by and representing members of a given community, conducts FPR, based on participatory diagnosis. Field days are held to allow wider participation in evaluating results and planning for further research. Work with cassava farmers in Brazil and with small-scale hillside farmers in Colombia demonstrates the effectiveness of this approach.

4. Researchers provide new materials and information to farmers, who then individually test and adapt innovations to their particular needs and situations. Forage research in Asia and farmers' independent experiments with green manure and cover crops in Uganda have led to systems-level innovations unforeseen by researchers.

5. Farmer participatory research is combined with innovations in the local institutional structure to further empower local communities and to allow communities to find

new, needed ways to interact with each other and with outside agencies. Organizing upper and lower watershed users in Colombia allowed a change from apparently conflicting resource-use interests to negotiation and eventual work toward mutual benefits. Successful initiation and organizing of small-farmer seed production in Uganda has led to recognizing the need for further institutional change in the seed sector.

The chapters in this volume document several types of success in FPR. First, as the above indicates, researchers working with farmers steadily made innovations in FPR itself. They improved methods and, overall, expanded the idea of participation from feedback from farmer-managed trials to the incorporation of farmers in problem diagnosis, selection of research problems, and community-based evaluation of results, leading to local choice in the direction of further experimentation. The encouragement and documentation of farmers' independent experiments based around introduced "unfinished" technology components reflects a growing respect for farmer traditional knowledge, farmers' natural tendency to experiment to solve problems, and the idea that only farmers can adapt innovations to particular local conditions. Finally, participation has started to encompass institutional change and local empowerment.

The second success and impact of FPR has been increased adoption of the approach by partner NARS. The work in Brazil, conducted by a wide range of NARS, began with a great deal of skepticism and ended with NARS changing policy in favor of using FPR in most, if not all, on-farm research. The research networks and consortia functioning in Asia are expressly working to institutionalize FPR and systems approaches throughout the region. Much of the effort to date has been both in the conduct of field projects and in training (of trainers, extension workers, researchers, and, importantly, NARS decision makers). The development of committees for local agricultural research in Colombia has led to both projects and NARS in several countries of Latin America adopting the approach.

Third, the different forms of FPR are clearly effective and efficient in solving agricultural problems in an integrated and locally appropriate fashion; and such effectiveness is starting to have impact through adoption of technologies and the benefits brought about by such adoption. The adaptation and adoption of new crops, varieties, legume-based improved NRM at the local level, pest and crop management practices, and livestock feeding systems are described in the various chapters.

Fourth, FPR appears to lead to greater farmer confidence in their own abilities, first in the conduct of problem-solving research, and later in new organizational and management skills. Recognition and encouragement of farmers' experiments, organized or not, has led to greater farmer-researcher interaction and increases in research efficiency.

The various papers have also identified constraints to effective FPR.

Obviously, in many cases, researchers need to provide sound, appropriate technical alternatives. Examples are cassava varieties that are actually superior to local varieties in Brazil, *Arachis* cultivars suited to poorer soils in the Colombian forest margins, or contour hedgerow species such as broom grass and lemon grass, which can bring real economic benefits. Once alternatives are identified as viable and valuable, planting materials often need to be made available. Lack of cassava planting materials in Asia and lack of legume seed in many projects has slowed the rate of FPR work at a time when farmer enthusiasm was relatively high.

For projects having a predetermined set of technology innovations (e.g., soil erosion control measures, legume cover crops, and green manure), sites and participating farmers must be carefully selected. Those more likely to participate are farmers suffering from, recognizing, and trying to solve the problem to be addressed (i.e., soil erosion or a need for improved nutrient cycling). Real and effective participation does not occur if farmers are not interested in the given problem. As a variation on the need to properly select sites and participants, the work in the Colombian forest margins encountered the interesting case of lack of effective participation because farm managers were not owners; the owners being largely absentee.

National agricultural research systems and local development or extension workers must have sufficient interest, training, commitment, and resources to work with farmers. They need to make field visits, provide (at times) farmer training, initially help organize local agricultural research groups or support individual experiments, and help farmers with evaluation and further planning. Lack of financial and institutional support can grind FPR projects to a halt.

Projects "tied" to particular commodities and/or management innovations may be unable or unprepared to work with farmers on their more pressing problems and needs. Such a limitation may result in farmers' lack of interest in participating in the project. A solution has been to increase the web and reach of participating institutions. The work in the hillsides of the Cauca Valley organized all interested external agencies to coordinate efforts and resources to better address the range of local needs and problems.

Agricultural research appears to be at an intermediate stage in terms of impact. Farmer participatory research methods are being developed and tested, and integrated into the work of partner NARS. Farmers in project communities are empowered to both experiment and deal more effectively with outside agencies. And new technical and organizational innovations are being adopted at project sites. The most important impact, however, is in the future: wider use of FPR beyond project areas, wider adaptation and adoption of technical alternatives developed, and local benefits derived by participating farmers and society as a whole.

The strategy for reaching such impact is to continue projects that lead to strengthening the integration of FPR approaches in NARS; and then, and with more difficulty, to find ways of achieving wider impact with less initial support. That is, the important question remains as to how to achieve wider impact with less initial project support and "hand holding". The move toward devolution of power and responsibilities to local communities in many areas of the world and as a philosophy of increasing numbers of development and donor agencies may be the needed steps in the right direction.

New Forms of Team and Partnership Research

Each of the projects described in this volume reflects interdisciplinary teamwork and partnerships with NARS, NGOs, and others. Teams ranged from collaborations of agronomists and geographers/GIS specialists to teams comprised of entomologists, plant breeders, pathologists, social scientists, soil scientists, livestock and forage specialists, and agronomists. Projects have ranged from international center collaboration with a major NARS, to partnerships among international centers, various NARS, universities (both local and international), NGOs, and local organizations. CIAT researchers in Asia, Africa, and Latin America have also helped to propose, seek funding for, and develop research networks and consortia intended to work on systems, employ FPR methods, and promote both international center-NARS partnerships and effective partnerships among participating countries. Partnership research reflects the fact that CIAT and its partners have comparative advantages in different complementary areas, and that partnerships are integral to promoting the sustainability of new ways of conducting research by the NARS.

As in the use of systems approaches, the projects described in this volume were designed as team and partnership based activities. As such, the papers did not address the lack of such partnerships in other projects. Certainly, however, funding for international agricultural research now supports new and more inclusive partnership relationships. Support has dried up for the lone international center scientist conducting independent research. Support is lessening for bilateral center-NARS agreements, but is increasing for proposals for partnerships among international centers, the various NARS (e.g., ministries and departments of agriculture, forestry, and natural resources rather than only agriculture), NGOs, and local community groups. The chapters

appear to indicate that progress is being made and that, in terms of strategy, although progress may have initially been rather "donor driven", current steps forward are being taken because of the demonstrated benefits for all of doing so.

Finally, agricultural research appears to have reached mid-stream, but is still making a crossing in the right direction. Germplasm and NRM research will continue to be conducted separately where appropriate (e.g., in generating new breeding lines or in monitoring the effects of current land uses on greenhouse gas emissions or biodiversity). In helping to solve problems where small-scale farmers want increases in production and in systems' sustainability, and where society also has desired outcomes, the integration of germplasm and NRM research is natural, appropriate, even obvious. A crucial future goal of systems research (reaching the far side of the stream) will be to develop effective ways of dealing with trade-offs between local or farmer goals for increased productivity and societal goals of maintaining the global environment.

Although not addressed in this volume, CIAT's work on systems also includes analyses of policies that have contributed to current resource use patterns at different scales, affected farmer adoption of different types of innovations, and sought a balance between increased productivity and environmental protection. A goal of such research is to be able to inform policymakers as to the effects of policy on NRM decisions at various levels.

The projects have shown a trend of improvements in FPR models. The challenge will be to make the participation of farmers and local communities more self-sufficient and self-sustaining. While local empowerment in its various forms appears to be the model for the future, considerable "political will" is needed to facilitate wide-reaching genuine change. In forming effective teams and partnerships, however, agricultural research seems to be nearing the far side of the stream. New partnerships and new types of partnerships (and new forms of funding) are emerging as effective—at first acceptable and now desirable by participating researchers and institutions.

A future volume on this topic will hopefully demonstrate that with few missteps the goals identified here will have been reached and what has already been achieved will have been consolidated and furthered.

Acronyms and Abbreviations Used in the Text

Acronyms

AC#3 — Agroforestry College no. 3 of the Thai Nguyen University, Vietnam

ADC — Agribusiness Development Center, Uganda

AMCAPI — Asociación de Mujeres Campesinas del Pital, Colombia

AusAID — Australian Agency for International Development

BES — Bohol Experiment Station, Philippines

BKTWG — Budama Kyelema Turbana Women's Group, Uganda

BMZ — Bundesministerium für Wirtschaftliche Zusammenarbeit und Entwicklung, Germany

BORIF — Bogor Research Institute for Food Crops, Indonesia

CAB International — Centre for Agriculture and Biosciences International, UK

CATAS — Chinese Academy of Tropical Agricultural Sciences

CATIE — Centro Agronómico Tropical de Investigación y Enseñanza, Costa Rica

CECIL — Centro de Estudios para la Conservación Integral de la Ladera, Colombia

CGIAR — Consultative Group on International Agricultural Research, USA

CIALs — Comités de Investigación Agrícola Local, Colombia (*Spanish for* CLARs)

CIDICCO — Centro Internacional de Información sobre Cultivos de Cobertura, Honduras

CIIFAD — Cornell International Institute for Food, Agriculture, and Development, USA (*of* Cornell University)

CIMMYT — Centro Internacional de Mejoramiento de Maíz y Trigo, Mexico

CIPASLA — Consorcio Interinstitucional para una Agricultura Sostenible en Laderas, Colombia

CIRAD — Centre de coopération internationale en recherche agronomique pour le développement, France

CLARs — Committees for Local Agricultural Research, Colombia (*English for* CIALs)

CNI — Centro Nacional de Investigación, Colombia

CNPMA — Centro Nacional de Pesquisa de Monitoramento e Avaliação de Impacto Ambiental (*of* EMBRAPA)

CNPMF	Centro Nacional de Pesquisa de Mandioca e Fruticultura Tropical (*of* EMBRAPA)
CODESU	Corporación para el Desarrollo Sostenible de Ucayali, Peru
COHDEFOR	Corporación Hondureña de Desarrollo Forestal
COLCIENCIAS	Instituto Colombiano para el Desarrollo de la Ciencia y la Tecnología "Francisco José de Caldas"
CORPOICA	Corporación Colombiana de Investigación Agropecuaria
CPAC	Centro de Pesquisa Agropecuária dos Cerrados (*of* EMBRABA)
CPACT	Centro de Pesquisa Agropecuária de Clima Temperado (*of* EMBRAPA)
CPATSA	Centro de Pesquisa Agropecuária do Trópico Semi-Árido (*of* EMBRAPA)
CSIRO	Commonwealth Scientific and Industrial Research Organisation, Australia
CURLA	Centro Universitario Regional del Litoral Atlántico, Honduras
CVC	Corporación Autónoma Regional del Valle del Cauca, Colombia
DOA	Department of Agriculture, Thailand
DOAE	Department of Agricultural Extension, Thailand
EBDA	Empresa Bahiana de Agricultura, Brazil
EMATER-CE	Empresa de Pesquisa, Assistência Técnica e Extensão Rural do Ceará, Brazil
EMATER-PB	Empresa de Pesquisa, Assistência Técnica e Extensão Rural do Paraíba, Brazil
EMATER-PE	Empresa de Pesquisa, Assistência Técnica e Extensão Rural do Pernambuco, Brazil
EMBRAPA	Empresa Brasileira de Pesquisa Agropecuária, Brazil
EMDAGRO	Empresa de Desenvolvimento Agropecuário de Sergipe, Brazil
EMEPA	Empresa Estadual de Pesquisa Agropecuária da Paraíba, S.A., Brazil
EPACE	Empresa de Pesquisa Agropecuária do Ceará, Brazil
FAO	Food and Agriculture Organization of the United Nations, Italy
FCRI	Field Crops Research Institute, Thailand
FEBESURCA	Federación de Beneficiarios de la Subcuenca de Cabuyal, Colombia
FIDAR	Fundación para la Investigación y el Desarrollo Agrícola, Colombia
FSP	Forages for Smallholders Project (*of* AusAID)
GRN	Grupo de Recursos Naturales (*of* CIMMYT)
GSCRI	Guangxi Subtropical Crops Research Institute, China
GTZ	Deutsche Gesellschaft für Technische Zusammenarbeit, Germany
IAS	Institute of Agricultural Sciences, Vietnam
IBFA	Ikulwe Bean Farmers' Association, Uganda
IBSRAM	International Board for Soil Research and Management, Thailand
ICA	Instituto Colombiano Agropecuario, Colombia
ICRAF	International Centre for Research in Agroforestry, Kenya

IDB	Inter-American Development Bank, USA		ORSTOM	Institut français de recherche scientifique pour le développement en coopération (*formerly* Office de la recherche scientifique et technique d'Outre Mer), France
IDEA	Investment in Developing Export Agriculture, Uganda			
IFAD	International Fund for Agricultural Development, Italy		PABRA	Pan-African Bean Research Alliance, Uganda
IFDC	International Fertilizer Development Center, USA		PASOLAC	Programa de Agricultura Sostenible de Laderas en Centro América (*of* IICA)
IFPRI	International Food Policy Research Institute, USA		PDBL	Proyecto Desarrollo Bosque Latifoliado, Honduras
IGN	Instituto Geográfico Nacional, Honduras			
IHCAFE	Instituto Hondureño del Café		PRCRTC	Philippine Root Crop Research and Training Center
IICA	Instituto Interamericano de Cooperación para la Agricultura, Costa Rica		PROFISMA	Proteção Fitossanitária Sustentável de Mandioca, Brazil (*Subproject of the CGIAR's project on* "Ecologically Sustainable Cassava Plant Protection in South America and Africa: An Environmentally Sound Approach" [ESCaPP])
IITA	International Institute of Tropical Agriculture, Nigeria			
INIAA	Instituto Nacional de Investigación Agraria y Agroindustrial, Peru			
IPA	Empresa Pernambucana de Pesquisa Agropecuária, Brazil		PRONATA	Programa Nacional de Transferencia, Colombia
IPRA	Investigación Participativa en Agricultura/*Participatory Research in Agriculture* (*of* CIAT)		PROSERTAO	Projeto de Apoio as Famílias de Baixa Renda da Região Semi-Árida, Brazil
ISNAR	International Service for National Agricultural Research, Netherlands		PUDOC	Centrum voor Landbouwpublikaties en Landbouwdocumentatie, Netherlands
IVITA	Instituto Veterinario de Investigaciones Tropicales y de Altura, Peru		RILET	Research Institute for Legumes and Tuber Crops, Indonesia
MWG	Makhai Women's Group, Uganda		SADC	Southern Africa Development Community
NARO	National Agricultural Research Organization, Uganda		SAG	Sociedad de Agricultores y Ganaderos del Valle del Cauca, Colombia
NSFI	National Soil and Fertilizer Institute, Vietnam		SDC	Swiss Agency for Development and Corporation
ODI	Overseas Development Institute, London		SECPLAN	Secretaría de Planificación, Coordinación y Presupuesto, Honduras

TAC	Technical Advisory Committee (*of the* CGIAR)
TROPILECHE	Sistemas de Alimentación a Base de Leguminosas Mejoradas para Pequeños Productores con Ganado de Doble Propósito en América Latina Tropical (*project of the* CGIAR)
UCRI	Upland Crops Research Institute, China
UEC	Universidade Estadual do Ceará, Brazil
UFAL	Universidade Federal de Alagoas, Brazil
UFBA	Universidade Federal da Bahia, Brazil
UMATAs	Unidades Municipales de Asistencia Técnica Agropecuaria, Colombia
UNCED	United Nations Conference on Environment and Development
UNDP	United Nations Development Programme
UNIBRAW	Brawijaya University, Indonesia
UNICAMP	Universidade Estadual de Campinas, Brazil

Abbreviations

AI	artificial insemination
ALS	angular leaf spot
ANT	anthracnose
AU	animal unit (*one cow and calf*)
B	black bean
BCMV	bean common mosaic virus
C	cassava
CBB	common bacterial blight
CGM	cassava green mite
CVAs	cropping systems, varieties, and agronomic practices
CVMV	cassava vein mosaic virus

d	data and maps
DM	dry matter
DMSO	dimethyl sulfoxide
DSSAT	Decision Support System for Agrotechnology Transfer crop simulation models
DTF	days to flowering
DTM	days to maturity
ESU	extensive sedentary upland
FGOs	few good options
FIE	farmers' independent experimentation
FP	number of farmers preferring ...
FPR	farmer participatory research
FSEs	farmer seed enterprises
FYM	farmyard manure
G	grassland
GxE	genotype x environment
GIS	geographic information systems
GMCCs	green manure and cover crops
HB	halo blight
i	key information and observations
IARCs	international agricultural research centers
IPM	integrated pest management
IRR	internal rates of return
ISU	intensive sedentary upland
LWG	liveweight gain
masl	meters above sea level
na	not applicable
NARS	national agricultural research systems
nd	no data
NGOs	nongovernment organizations
NP	ρ-nitrophenol

NRM	natural resource management	RRAs	rapid rural appraisals
P	peanut; plantation	S&B	slash-and-burn (*agricultural system*)
P_i	productivity index (*for soils*)	SD	standard deviation
PCR	polymerase chain reaction	SOM	soil organic matter
PD	participatory diagnosis	SP	sweetpotato
PDR	People's Democratic Republic	SQIs	soil quality indicators
PE	participatory evaluation	SSP	single superphosphate fertilizer
PR	participatory research	T	taro
PTD	participatory technology development	TAs	technical assistants
R&D	research and development	TOT	training of trainers (*course in FPR methodologies in Vietnam*)
RFL	rainfed lowland	U Sh	Ugandan shilling